The leaves of
elnofull at
the page.

1

Here Come the Land Girls

With Best Wishes,

To Louise,

From.

Eve Dieth

Here Come the Land Girls

Eve Diett

HERE COME THE LAND GIRLS

INTRODUCTION

"THE LAND GIRL"

To be a Land Girl was a challenge every day, every way.

At times when harsh weather prevailed, we would question why from day to day.

Some days were filled with laughter, others sad, we shed our tears, we hid our fears.

Without the Land Girl to till his land, where would the farmer have been without his right hand?

So I dedicate this book to all the ex-Land Girls throughout the land, just to say we are not a forgotten army, a forgotten band.

Evelyn

Dedication

To my late husband Bill

Contents

CHAPTER ONE
HERE COME THE LAND GIRLS

It was April 1942 when I went to join up. The recruiting officer entered the room, a rather daunting figure. She was a well-built lady with her hair scraped back into a bun, around middle age at a guess. My God, she was grim; I was scared to death. She was wearing a green jacket over a heavy tweed skirt and lilac check stockings.

'Well, young lady, come this way,' she said, opening the waiting room door. I was ushered in. 'Wait here Miss until I send for you,' she informed me.

I looked around the room; it was austere, apart from the brightly coloured posters which adorned the walls. One was of a sailor with a kit bag slung over one shoulder, with the wording:

"ON THE HOME FRONT,
CARELESS TALK COSTS LIVES"

The next one was:

"IS YOUR JOURNEY REALLY NECESSARY?"

I read that once again and wondered if I should take flight before the grim old maid came for me.

I began to wonder if I had gone over the top with my dress. For this great occasion I was wearing a stylish new cotton dress that my aunt had made for me, a red and black pleated skirt with a splash of poppies on the bodice. I had borrowed my friend's high-heeled sandals, and to complete the picture my hair was piled on top with two ringlets hanging over my forehead, which after all was the fashion, and looked great on Veronica Lake, the film star. The whole idea of this operation was to look sophisticated and to look

1

older than my 16½ years, but by the look of the recruiting officer I began to doubt having my nerve to tell a lie, for to join the Women's Land Army the minimum age was 17½!

My gaze went to another poster. This one was of a Land Girl smiling as though she was advertising toothpaste. She was dressed in uniform which consisted of a green V-necked pullover, khaki breeches, woollen socks which came just below the knees, and with heavy brogue shoes, one of which was resting on a spade. Above was the heading:

"DIGGING FOR VICTORY
YOUR COUNTRY NEEDS YOU"

I glanced down at my dress and dainty sandals. *Well,* I asked myself, *are you prepared to swap your dress style for that?* I had not given much thought to what the Land Girls would wear.

I knew it was the better of two evils, the first being the munitions factory, for I was too young for the forces; so really it was my only chance to escape working long hours, being shut in all day, with the noise and soul-destroying work, and not forgetting the danger from air raids.

The recruiting officer ushered me into her office. She gave me a faint smile, which softened her severe looks. I took in three deep breaths and thought, *Well, here goes, Eve, now put on a great performance.*

'Right then Evelyn, pull a chair up here at the desk. I have been looking at your application form and everything looks pretty straightforward. Tell me, why The Land Army? I should have thought the Wrens or the WAAFs would have been more suitable for you. After all, you are not really built for farm life, you are rather on the skinny side;' but then she added with a throaty chuckle, 'with those long legs and arms, quick up the ladder, eh what? So, I will enlist you, dear, for Market Gardening. Do you agree, Evelyn?' she said.

'Well, I did rather hope I would work with animals,' I replied.

'Try the Market Gardening first, then at a later date go on to the General Farming – break you in gently, eh what?' she said.

Personally, I did not care for the "break in gently" remark, I wanted to reply, 'I'm not a horse!'

She tapped her pen on the desk then she stood up, smoothing down the front of her tweed skirt. 'Well,' she said with gusto, 'that's that – now come over to the window dear, let's get you measured up for your uniform.'

'Have I been accepted then?' I asked.

'Well, yes,' she replied, 'if you pass the medical – and also you will need two references.' She added, 'You are of age are you not?'

My heart sank, and my stomach did a double flip. 'Yes, yes,' I lied.

'17½, well, don't look so worried, I can assure you, my dear, you will soon have the pleasure of joining all the other splendid young ladies who are doing this country a great service – eh what?'

I think she must have been a member of "The Jolly Hockey Sticks" club, but after all, she was a good sport. 'What Ho!' But my, those lilac stockings, they were something else!

*

I returned a week later with the references and medical certificate. Obtaining the latter was a hilarious event, the

3

doctor had me running around the surgery in my knickers, and jumping up and down. Just as well I was not over-endowed bust wise, as I might have ended up with two black eyes! On the other hand, it was most embarrassing, I was so nervous that I had great difficulty doing up my bra strap.

He leered at me, 'Come over here Miss.'

'Er, n-no thank you Doctor, I can manage,' I stuttered.

'Silly girlie – now come on, I see all shapes and sizes every day and you have nothing to be ashamed of.'

I retrieved the medical certificate from his desk and then shot out of there quicker than I went in. It would not have been of any use to complain in those days, no one would have believed you.

I managed to convince my mother that joining The Women's Land Army was a better option, being out in the fresh air every day, than the dreaded munitions factory. She was more worried about "The bum lot" I would be mixing with.

*

The day came for me to begin my debut as a Land Girl. I had said my goodbyes to my work colleagues, in the office where I had been employed for a year. They thought I was crazy, and were of the same mind as my family, that I would only last a month or so. But I was determined to prove them wrong.

I met the other "splendid young ladies" at the local station picking-up point, they were a friendly lot. Many of the girls were from Birmingham, some from Bristol, and I was the only one from Worcester. We had plenty of time to become acquainted with one another because the lorry driver was late collecting us. When eventually he did arrive he greeted us with 'Bleeding 'ell – how am I going to fit you all in the back?'

Rose, the jolly girl from the Birmingham group shouted, 'You will find a way Spike. Me and Hilda here,' pointing to her friend, 'we'll sit up in the cab with you.'

He was a thin spotty youth with hair that stood up in spikes. 'Looks like he just fell out of bed,' said one of the other girls with Rose.

'Well, come on ladies, all aboard. Let's get the show on the road.'

'Where are we off to then, Spike?' Rose asked.

'Bloody mystery tour,' he replied.

'Very funny, ha ha,' they all chorused.

'Bleeding jokers we have here,' remarked Hilda.

'Keep ya hair on Spike,' they shouted.

We were tossed from side to side in the back of the Army lorry, as we sat on the wooden side benches. Most uncomfortable! We all sang, *"Show me the way to go home"*, and *"It's a long way to Tipperary"*. I was wedged in between Rose and her friend Hilda, who were well upholstered, so I fared better than some.

Eventually, we pulled off the road into a long winding drive guarded by tall wrought iron gates. We passed rose bushes, various shrubs and trees, and it was surrounded by thick undergrowth that seemed to go on forever.

'Hang in there ladies,' shouted Spike, 'don't get excited, I may have taken the wrong turning.'

*

Peacocks were strutting around calling out in greetings! Then there is was . . . majestic, high and wide . . . spreading over several acres, with wings jutting off east and west. Four impressive pillars supported a gracious front porch.

Spike pulled up at the entrance and exclaimed, 'I think we have come to the wrong place, it don't look like any hostel to me.' Jumping down from the cab he called back, 'Stay seated ladies, I'll go and suss it out.'

We all hoped it was the end of our journey because we were all baking in our thick uniforms. My feet felt like lead weights in the brogue shoes, after all it was mid August and very hot with the sun beating down on the canvas roof of the lorry.

Spike pulled on the wrought iron bell that was situated at the left of the large impressive oak doors. We could hear it echoing through the place. It was opened by an elderly lady in a green blazer, followed by two younger ladies who came over to introduce themselves to us. Miss Roberts was the housekeeper; a smile of unaffected friendship radiated from her handsome face and her greying hair was scraped back into a French pleat. She made me feel more at ease at once. She beckoned to Spike to come over and let the back flap of the lorry down so that she could get us all indoors, out of the stifling heat, for refreshments.

'Welcome to the Manor, all you young girls. You are our very first guests,' she said, 'eventually there will be 100. Rose and her friends looked around the place in amazement.

'Rather grand,' remarked Hilda, 'hope we do not have to dress for dinner.'

'Don't be ignorant,' exclaimed Meg, 'we ain't going to have cocktails.'

We were ushered into the main hall, then led up the grand winding staircase by Janet, the maid, to our allotted rooms. I was in Chintz Room with Meg, Rose, Hilda, Mary and Vera. It was heaven to change into something cool and part company with the shoes. Janet appeared at the door.

'Come on you girls, Miss Roberts wants you all to assemble in the hall right away.' We quickly made our way down the stairs.

Miss Roberts told us the rules of the house, which were:

1. All beds to be made before leaving for work, all valuables and clothes to be neatly put away in drawers or lockers provided.

2. On returning from work, shoes or gumboots to be removed at back door, cleaned and lined up on the rack. Dirt and debris from the farm to be shaken from jackets and dungarees outside.

3. No running along the corridors or staircases. No sliding down the banisters.

4. Everyone to be in by 10 o'clock, unless a late pass (maximum of one per month) is requested.

5. Morning call is at 6.30 am, breakfast at 7 am, at which time packed lunches for the day are to be collected. Evening meal 7 pm sharp.

6. No visitors – unless by special request. In the case of male friends, you are to say goodnight to them at the main gates.

7. Wages are 12/6d a week.

Many of the girls muttered, 'It's like being at school.' I looked around me and thought, *I wonder how many will stick it out.*

So we began our first day as Land Girls.

We slept in bunks, Meg slept on the bottom and I was on top, well, most of the time. I could never get the hang of it and fell out most nights. So it was with reluctance that Meg changed with me, but she had to agree it was a good idea, and made a change from my foot in her face when I made my sleepy descent.

*

Our first job on the farm was fruit picking. I thought, *Well, if all goes to plan my long arms and legs will stand me in good stead, - eh what?'* It was fine for a week, we stuffed ourselves with the best fruit and ended up with the trots!

Then boredom set in, so to liven things up we would take it in turns to ride on the backs of the young heifers in the yard, to see who could stay on the longest. We ended up with sore heads and bruises in various places too delicate to mention. We were all sick of plums and apples.

At last we were allowed to hold our first dance in the very grand ballroom at the hostel. To say just "grand" did not do it justice. It had mirrors around the room from ceiling to floor, all gilt edged. I could imagine in days gone by the splendours that took place, and I could hear the rustle of the ladies' ball gowns, as they glided past in the arms of their handsome partners.

Our partners were going to be the local RAF airmen from the nearby station. We were all looking forward to it with great anticipation. It was with great excitement that we went shopping with our precious clothing coupons. My coupons, to my dismay, were not enough for the blue taffeta dress of my dreams. So, I went in the dress my aunt had made me, and I borrowed from one of the girls a pair of red high-heeled peep toe shoes, which matched the poppies on

8

the bodice of the dress. To complete the picture I painted my toenails red.

After this great event we were sent to a farm to pick potatoes behind the tractor, which meant on a windy day we would eat dust and soil. Our eyes stung, not to mention our aching backs. At this stage Rose kicked her bucket and protested that the farmer could "stick his potatoes up his Khyber pass and 'er was back off to Brum".

Hilda had a crush on one of the farm hands so she had no problem filling her bucket. They say love is blind, and on this occasion it must have been, for he was a shady character who always had a dewdrop hanging from his nostrils, which kept going up and down when he sniffed, which was often. We all wondered what happened when he held her close and kissed her! There was no reply from Meg and Rose but looks spoke volumes.

From his stained corduroy trousers, tied up with string, he produced a tobacco tin, a packet of Rizla cigarette papers, and taking a long sniff with the dewdrop just hovering on the end of his nose, he gazed longingly at Hilda. He walked towards her saying, ' 'ilda, would ee like a fag?'

She looked up at him – there were tears of love in her eyes, 'Oh Arthur,' and he lifted her up and humped her onto the trailer with the potato sacks, and proceeded to roll her a cigarette. By now the dewdrop was going up and down with great speed.

I was fascinated by this scene, so was oblivious to my task in hand until a voice shouted, 'Cum on, what yer think yer doing? You ain't on yer 'olidays!' Come on, get yer backs down, let's see if we can get these tatters picked up today.' And to the two love birds he retorted, 'Put 'er down Arfur, and get yer arse over 'ere and load them full sacks on trailer.' He joked, 'What did yer Ma feed you for breakfast lad? Whatever it was I could do with a basin full.'

Being that the farmhouse was too far away the question arose of where to go to "spend a penny". The farmhands, we noted, jumped over the fence and into the next field. We all held a discussion on this. I lost the toss so was nominated to approach the farmer. He looked at me with his mouth open and replied, 'Same as t'others!'

I stood my ground. 'No, we need a proper toilet.'

He went red and purple with rage. I thought at any moment he was going to blow a gasket. When he did reply it was, 'Git back and pick them there tatters.'

Standing my ground I looked at him squarely in the face and said, 'No, I will not.'

Dew Drop Arthur piped in, ' 'fraid yer might git stung on nettles, hee hee?'

I gave him a black look and said to the farmer, without thinking whether the others would stand by me, 'If that is your answer to our request, you can pick your own potatoes.' He drew a sharp breath and turned even more purple.

As I turned to walk away he said, 'Cum back 'ere Miss, yer can 'ave yer toilet, where would yer like it put?' I asked in amazement if he really meant it. He grunted, 'It makes sense, don't want 'ee all vanishing over edge, it ain't decent.'

Leading the farmhands round the back of the lorry he gave them each a spade and said, 'Dig an 'ole at far end of field.' I made my way back to the others and watched in amazement.

Arthur said, 'Guv'nor, there be no more spades.'

'Use fork then, you silly bugger, and git on wi' it, and tell Ernie to go to the farm and bring tarpaulin and some newspapers and string,' replied the farmer.

We all thought that while this was going on we would rest. But alas, no; he called me over and said, 'Git into tractor and take her steady.' I protested that I couldn't drive. 'Now's the time to learn,' was the reply. I prayed that they would finish building the loo in record time, before I reached the end of the field, for I had visions of going straight through the far off hedge into the field beyond. In the confusion I had forgotten to ask where the brake was.

I could feel a trickle of sweat on my brow and was getting very near to the end of the row when, to my relief, the farmer jumped up behind me. He pulled on the brake, and beaming from ear to ear and puffing out his chest said, 'We 'ave finished the toilet for you young gals, go git over there and sees if ye like it.'

I walked towards it sensing with out looking back that they were all waiting for my approval. Attached to the front, tied on securely with string was a large piece of cardboard, and written in large letters in red paint were the words:

"LADIES ONLY"

Lifting the flap I went in not quite knowing what to expect. I was horrified to see before me just a gaping black hold with wooden hand rails each side – presumably to hold on to with legs astride! My imagination ran riot – what would happen when your dungarees were round your ankles and you did not have perfect balance – it did not bear thinking about. On each side of the rails was newspaper neatly cut into squares, hanging on a string.

Beckoning to the girls to come and look Rose said she would sooner risk going over the hedge. All the others

11

nodded in agreement, so I went to the farmer. I explained our dilemma and said we all appreciated what he and his men had done for us but please could we have some wooden planks across the hole, just in case we were unfortunate enough to slip in, especially if the earth got wet.

'Arr,' he replied, 'that were on my mind to do just that.' So back off to the farm they went and came back with the planks. We were much happier when they were installed.

'Now,' said the farmer, puffing out his chest, 'be it all to yer liking? Can we git on and git these tatters up?' We finished two days early, so with gratitude we were all given half a crown each, for he was able to get to the market in time to sell his potatoes. We all said our goodbyes, then on we went to the next farm.

*

This farmer had all kinds of modern equipment which he had designed himself. One machine in particular was a trailer built up with a conveyor belt with four seats on it, two each side, with ridges on the belt in which to place cabbage plants. The idea was for the four of us to place the plants in each ridge, then they would rotate, and underneath was a scoop like a spade, that pushed the plants into the earth. The young lad who was driving the tractor for this contraption was named Ginger. Rose teased him mercilessly. The poor lad went as red as his hair. We sat two each side of this machine then placed the cabbage plants on the belt as it went around.

We were all so busy talking and teasing him, and being that it was so damned boring we were oblivious to what was happening. We had covered half the field before we realised all the roots were sticking up in the air.

Ginger was very agitated. He jumped down from the tractor shouting, 'You have just got to go and pick them all up, and we will start again before the Guv'nor comes back from market.'

We collected two rows of cabbage plants when there was a downpour. We made a dash for the barn. Ginger was jumping up and down shouting, 'Come back, you can't leave it like this.'

'Not bleeding likely,' said Rose.

Meg shouted over to him, 'Come with us Ginger, we will tell the farmer it was all our fault.' He threw his hands into the air, gave the contraption a good kick, and then followed us into the barn.

The farmer said, 'Finished already?'

We replied, 'Well, something went very wrong, the roots ended up in the air instead of in the ground.'

There was a look of disbelief on his face. 'Well now, you could not have been paying attention to your task in hand,' he said. Then to Ginger he retorted, 'What the bloody hell were you doing when all this was going on?'

The poor boy stammered, 'I-I could not see what they were doing back there Guv'nor.'

'But you were driving the sodding tractor,' replied the farmer, 'and I don't see you wearing blinkers.'

Looking over at us he said, 'Well, I think you'd better have the rest of the day off, and I don't think it would be of any possible interest to you or me, so let's have your time sheets. We'll put you down for the day, after all it is unfair to put all the blame on your heads, you are far too young to cope with a man's work.'

We felt remorse for not doing the job properly, and for letting them both down after the treatment we had experienced from some of the other farmers.

'He appeared to be a good sort,' Rose remarked, 'I don't expect he will forget us in a hurry.'

I laughed and said, 'Well, I won't forget those roots waving in the air and the look of shock on Ginger's face!'

* * *

CHAPTER TWO
SANDFORD FARM

After the cabbage plant disaster, we were sent to another farm near the hostel. To get there we had to cross two fields. One field (they were not sure which one) had a bull in it, so their advice was to play safe and skirt around the edge of the fields near the fences, so there would be plenty of room if escape were needed.

To accompany me on this job were Madge, Meg and Rose. The work consisted of weeding onions, which at a guess we knew would be a backbreaking task, so we were not looking forward to it. The next morning when we set out there was a complete grey blanket of fog.

'Well, for one thing,' said Rose, 'the bull will have great difficulty seeing us in this pea-souper.' We walked through the centre of the first field.

'Where's the stile?' called out Meg.

'How the hell do we know,' retorted Rose, 'just keep heading straight.'

'But we can't see anything,' called out Meg, 'what if the bull is in front of us?'

'Don't worry about the front,' shouted out Rose, 'it's the rear you've got to worry about, if you hear him, run like hell!'

We could just about make out the welcoming outline of the stile through the fog. I was last in the line waiting my turn to clamber over when there was an almighty snort from behind me. I did no more than shout out, 'Quick! The bull is behind me.'

I did not hang around, I jumped over the stile, losing my lunch box in the scramble. I felt sure I had only just made it. We all landed in one heap.

'Perhaps it's only a cow,' said Madge.

'Well, I wasn't going to stay behind to find out,' I retorted.

'I'll go to our house,' said Meg (it was a favourite saying of hers).

'You sure as hell would,' quipped Rose, 'if you had had his horns up your arse!'

*

We arrived at the farm all looking dishevelled; I was minus my food for the day and ended up with a sandwich from each of my friends. The farmer was a Mr Sandford, who was a miserable-looking individual, tall, about six foot, with spiky bits of hair sticking out of his ears. He had eyes that darted back and forth like a bird's, a long beak-like nose and a perpetual sneer on his thin lips. He wore a battered trilby hat pulled down over his forehead. His tatty corduroy trousers were tied up with string around the ankles. He chewed constantly on something that resembled a matchstick. He moved it around his lips with great speed when he was angry.

'Well, you gals,' he greeted us, 'you found us alright?'

'Yes,' we replied.

Rose piped in, 'Mr Sandford sir, we came the field way and we feel sure the bull was in there. Oh, and by the way Eve lost her lunch box when we all dived over the stile at the same time in fright.'

'Well, well, that'll teach yer to teck short cuts, git up early tomorrow and take the long way round. Land Girls!' he muttered under his breath. He gestured, 'This way to the onion field, I wants all weeds taking out, not a single one left behind now, got that?'

The fog was just lifting. There were rows and rows of the blasted onions. We looked at each other in despair. He indicated for us to kneel and take the weeds out and said, 'All weeds to be pulled out by hand, so down on your knees.'

We hesitated. 'Well?' he said, with the matchstick moving at great speed around his mouth, 'what yer waiting for, they aren't going to pop up to yer, it be the only way to do it. You,' he gestured to Rose, 'cum up to the barn and yer can bring back sacks to kneel on.'

We had two days doing that job. Our knees were bruised and sore, and when the breeze got up the dust from the soil went into our eyes. Madge wept and said she had had enough and would go back to Brum, and he could stick his onions up his arse! I think if the job had lasted any longer we would all have walked out, and to hell with the consequences.

*

Our next job after the onions was in the greenhouses planting seedlings and watering the tomato plants. You could only work for a short time in there because it was so hot and humid. We were all relieved when we moved on to the next farm.

Every Monday evening at the hostel we had German lessons. That was hilarious with Rose and her Brum accent. We did not learn any German when she was around. We wondered why they introduced these classes, were they by any chance looking ahead to the possibility of England losing the war and preparing us for that event, it was rather scary to even contemplate it. We all refused to think that way – to be positive was the thing to do.

'To go on every day with that thought niggling away in your mind would be no use,' said Rose, 'of course we are going to win, we have just got to bloody well think in that direction.'

*

On arriving back in the lorry from work the next day there was a police car at the hostel. Being ushered into the back seat were Margaret Stein, one of our Land Girls, with her sister, Anna. We knew them well, they usually sat at our table in the dining hall, and I had worked with Margaret on several occasions and found her very friendly. She had accompanied Rose and me to the dances at the RAF station several times too.

When I thought back, she was always interested in Don, the pilot air cadet I was friendly with, and she asked many questions about the aircraft on the station and quizzed Don on manpower and locations in the district. Don always changed the subject. I never answered any of her questions because at the end of the day there was nothing to relate, I just thought she was being over curious about everything. We did think they were a bit odd at times, because in all weathers they would cycle around the countryside after work every evening, except for Monday evenings when they were the star pupils in the German class. After they left, in such haste, so the German lessons folded.

We were all summoned to assemble in the main hall to be told by a police sergeant that Margaret and Anna were being held under suspicion of spying, along with their two brothers, who had been followed by the police to a deserted barn in the countryside and caught red-handed sending out messages to the enemy on a wireless transmitter.

The airmen on the nearby RAF station had orders not to visit the hostel, that it was "out of bounds" until further notice.

'Flipping typical,' said Rose, 'shutting the stable door after the horse has bolted!'

'No more socials or dances, we shall not have much to look forward to now,' Madge retorted, 'in this back wood of a place. It will be deadly.'

* * *

CHAPTER THREE
ICED SPROUTS

We had only been in the Land Army for two months so there was plenty of room for improvement. Many of the girls came from large cities, and it was a revelation to them, or should I say shock? Several were homesick and wept a lot. I found myself being an agony aunt.

One evening, on my way down to dinner I paused to look at the notice board. To my horror my name was there for sprout picking the next day, along with nine of my colleagues. I noted Rose's name on the list. It went on to say the lorry would be at the main gates at 7 am. We all arose the next morning early on this dreaded day, and made a beeline for the bathroom before the never-ending queue of sleepy heads. From there we went to the kitchen to pick up our lunch packs and flasks then had a quick breakfast in the large dining room, with everyone looking in a dazed state and no conversation. The only sound was the scraping of spoons against the cereal bowls.

Then after putting our feet very reluctantly into our cold gumboots, we donned our heavy Land Army jackets and staggered out into the frosty morn. It was now mid-October, the lorries were driven by Conscientious Objectors, young men with religious beliefs, or who objected to war in general and had chosen to do this job, which was the better of two evils, the other option being to work down the mines.

Our driver's name was Dick and he had the look of an insurance man, so we always had the feeling that he was going to issue out the policies, instead it was only our timesheets for the day.

'Good morning ladies,' said Dick in a cheery voice. It did nothing to jolt us out of our present mood, which was due to the thought of picking sprouts with icicles on.

We grunted back, 'Mornin'.'

With that we climbed aboard the lorry. Dick, whistling merrily, climbed into the cab and we rolled away down the drive, out towards those dreaded sprouts. The thought kept hammering in my brain, should I come clean about my age and escape all this, and return to the comforts of home? Then my rebellious spirit took over and I was determined to see it through.

Suddenly, Rose burst into a high-pitched giggle, 'Bleeding 'ell,' she said, 'you should se all your faces, just like dead ducks in a thunderstorm.' I looked around at the others, and we did look a sorry lot. Rose beamed at me and burst into song, singing, *"Daisy, Daisy, give me your answer do"*. We all joined in, stamping our cold feet to the rhythm. Before long, however, we arrived at the farm, and our circulation was working well even though the enthusiasm was lacking.

Dick came and lowered the flap, and out we jumped and huddled together. We did look a sorry sight standing there while Dick went in search of the farmer. We did not have to wait for long, the farmer walked towards us. He was a large ruddy-faced man with a purple nose.

He said, 'Mornin'.' With that we caught a whiff of his whisky-laden breath, it was overpowering.

'Well, let's 'ave timesheets,' he said gruffly. Without looking at them he stuffed them into his pocket. Beckoning for us to follow him his parting words to Dick were, 'Pick 'em up about 5.' My opinion of him was that he was an ignorant pig. I took a deep breath and followed behind with the others.

On coming to the field, I was horrified to see that it was vast, and the fog was still lingering over the land. The sprouts were thick with frost. Without looking at us he spoke, kicking at the hard earth. 'Nets are on yon trailer. When yer 'as filled them, leave 'em at end of rows and Charlie the foreman will pick 'em up.' With that he ambled away, leaving us with a scene like something from the ice age. Rose was all for skiving off down the nearest pub, 'Then the old bugger would get rid of us,' she said.

I protested, 'We cannot do that Rose, we must make the best of it and get started.'

'Yow must be off yowr 'ead,' was her reply.

'But it may only be for today,' I pleaded.

'Now I know yow's bleeding crackers, with all that lot to pick we could be 'ere for weeks.'

I must admit it did look daunting. But nevertheless I picked up the nets and handed them around. To my surprise they all followed me like lambs to the slaughter. I suppose in a way I took it upon myself to be the leader although I had never thought of myself as such, always being rather shy at school and never pushing to the fore. And after all I was the junior, but they did not know that and I never did enlighten them on that score.

I was secretly enjoying this newfound position. Rose looked at me and her face was transfigured, almost saintly. She suddenly put her arms around my shoulders saying to the others, 'Cum on then, let's do as Eve says and git on with it. We'll show the old bugger what we's made of.'

After steadily picking the ice-clad sprouts, we at last reached the end of one row. Our hands were sore and fingers swollen up like sausages. My feet, I thought, had given up the ghost on me and died. The silence was broken by Emily, sobbing. She was a very petite girl with delicate features, would have been more at home married to a rich man and being pampered.

Rose and I thought it would be a good idea if we did physical jerks halfway up each row to get our blood circulating. I put Rose in charge of the operation, she thoroughly enjoyed this and bullied and cajoled until everyone was in motion.

After our third row our fingers were so swollen that it was impossible to get any movement into them and the mist was descending fast, it was impossible to see more than a few yards. So then I "took the bull by the horns", as the saying goes, and stumbled my way towards the farmhouse to confront "Mr Pig".

On pausing to look back, my colleagues were lost in the mist. With great difficulty I trudged on until I came to the farmyard, but there was not a soul in sight, so I headed towards the farmhouse that lay back in a hollow. From the farm buildings, it looked eerie and unreal with the mist surrounding it. I walked around the buildings, then went over and knocked on the door of the farmhouse, and a voice from within answered, 'Come in.' The doors opened, I pushed the door and stumbled in. The voice said, 'I am in the kitchen.' I suddenly felt a pang of anxiety, but headed towards where the voice came from.

A small dark-haired woman stood in the doorway of the kitchen with a rolling pin in one hand, sleeves rolled up and hands thick with flour and pastry. We stood motionless and looked at one another. There was a look of disbelief in her face, then she spoke.

'Yer must be one of the Land Girls who came this morning to pick sprouts. My love, yer looks frozen, 'ave yer seen your face?' She pointed me towards a mirror which was hanging by the kitchen door. The face that looked back at me was like a being from the Arctic, with frost on my eyebrows and hair, and my nose shining like a red beacon.

The woman guided me towards the blazing fire, 'Get thawed out child.' She proceeded to fill a bowl with warm water, 'This be to put yer hands in, pain will be unbearable for a while, while they be thawing out. I pleaded with her that my friends were still down in the field and that please may I go and bring them up. 'Yer ain't going anywhere luv, I'll go and git Charlie, wait till 'ee gets back.' "Ee" – I presume was Mr Pig.

Indeed it was agony as I soaked my hands in the warm water, but gradually the blood flowed into my fingers, and with the warmth of the kitchen I was beginning to feel more human. I slipped out of my gumboots, sat in front of the large black range and toasted my feet back to life. It was heaven. The only noise to be heard was the ticking of the clock and the singing of the kettle on the hob. I surveyed the kitchen.

On the well-scrubbed kitchen table was pastry ready to be made into pies. An old grandfather clock stood in the far corner with the pendulum gently going back and forth; a peaceful scene. Another world away from the sprout field. With the warmth from the range I felt sleepy. I closed my eyes for a few seconds only to be jolted back to life by the sound of a tractor in the yard and footsteps in the passageway coming towards the kitchen.

In the wake of the little dark-haired woman my friends stumbled in, looking exactly as I had on my arrival. Emily was red-eyed and ghastly white, she was ushered to a chair by the woman, who began to rub Emily's hands, and I helped with the warm water in the bowl treatment for the others. Rose did not utter a word, which was most unusual. The only sound she made was an "Oh" and "Ah" when the feeling was painfully coming back into her hands.

I could not imagine the woman being the farmer's wife, and watching her being so kind and gentle with Emily made me curious. I approached her and very tactfully asked when her husband, the farmer, would return.

'My luv, 'ee ain't my husband, I'm only the housekeeper. Wouldn't want 'im for an 'usband – spends too much time in boozer. Today 'ee be at market, three sheets to the wind by now no doubt.' So to reassure me she went on, 'Don't 'ee worry luv, 'e'l not be back today. Yer can all stay and 'ave sum dinner wi' me. Then I'll git Charlie to give 'ee all a job in the barn, apple sortin'. But first we'll get something hot insides yer, 'ope 'ee likes rabbit stew with dumplings, and do call me Martha, for that be me name.'

We went to the barn later feeling warm inside, and our thanks to Martha – what a lovely woman. When Dick came at five to collect us, Martha came out and we reluctantly said our goodbyes to her.

Rose said, 'When yow gets fed up with 'im, cum to Brum. Me ma will 'ave you.'

So back to the hostel.

*

That night we had been invited to the local RAF station to a dance. With the events of the day forgotten, we began to discuss what we were going to wear. Not that there was a lot to choose from, as we were rationed with coupons to buy clothes, so you could use your whole quota on one dress. We had a good system going, and borrowed from each other, so that we did not wear the same thing twice. Silk stockings were only available on the black market at £1 each stocking, so we painted our legs with sand mixed with water into a paste, it worked quite well. We used black boot polish and Vaseline mixed together for mascara, but had to remember not to rub our eyes! I was fortunate enough to have an aunt who was a wizard with a needle – an excellent dressmaker. For a special event she produced an evening gown for me from a pair of curtains, and also made me a dressing gown from an old grey army blanket.

We were invited to the homes of the local people, also socials and dances at the nearby Army and Air Force camps. The war, in some ways, brought people closer together – there was the warmth and spirit that one remembered at Christmas, it was a feeling of belonging, it certainly made up for the hardships we had to endure on some farms and when the weather was rough. On our way out that evening we were informed by our housekeeper that we would not be going back to the sprout field, instead we would travel by cycle to a farm which was only 3 miles away from the hostel, and we were to be there for 7.30 am. Our party included Rose, so we knew for sure we would not have a dull moment.

*

On approaching the farmhouse, standing motionless in the doorway was the farmer, watching us with great interest as we cycled towards him, He was puffing madly on his pipe, so his whole face was engulfed in smoke.

We dismounted and walked towards him, he lowered his head, staring at his boots, and said, without looking up, 'Mornin', yer late.'

We went to open our mouths to protest that in fact we were early, for on looking at my watch it was 7.25 am, but he went on, still staring at his boots, 'Three of yer's in mangel field, other two horse hoeing.'

I managed to butt in and said, addressing him, 'Mr Jones, we have not had any experience with horses.'

Without looking up he replied, 'Well, that be very brave of yer to volunteer.' Lifting his head for a brief second he looked at me with his narrow snake-like eyes, still puffing away on his pipe, 'Tek 'er with yer,' he said, pointing to Rose. Then, beckoning to one of the farm hands who had been loitering around while this exciting conversation was going on, said, 'Eric, tek these two up to stables and give 'um Blossom ter work with, they'll just about manage 'er. With that his gaze went back to his boots.

We walked away following Eric, whom we later named "Windy", for with every step a rumble broke forth like an ack-ack gun. I did not dare to look at Rose at this precise time. On arriving at the stable, Eric opened back the large doors. It was almost pitch dark inside. Standing restlessly in a row were six very large Shire horses with enormous hoofs. My heart pounding, I stood frozen to the spot, with Rose behind me.

'Bleeding 'ell,' said Rose, 'I'm off with the others to pull mangels.' Gingerly we made our way alongside the horses.

Eric turned and said, 'Don't be afraid, they be gentle.' He went on to say that in future on coming into the stable we should always talk to them, for they could get very jumpy at sudden noises. That, needless to say, did nothing to allay my fear, in fact I was in the same state of mind as Rose. Eric beckoned for us to follow him, introducing us as he went along the line of horses.

'This one be Marigold, next be Pilot, an' 'ere be Blossom. Lovely old gal, 'er be.' She nuzzled Eric and he produced from his tattered corduroys a lump of sugar, passing it to me to give her. I laid my hand flat open with the sugar resting on my palm and Blossom's warm soft mouth closed over it.

Still crouching behind me was Rose. I turned and said, 'Rose, she is lovely, come and stroke her.'

'Not bleeding likely!' was her reply.

Eric proceeded to lead Blossom out of the stall. Handing the reins over to me he said, 'Urry up afore the Guv'nor cums back.' We caught up with him, with Blossom gently trotting beside me.

This time it was a field full of winter cabbages, there was a railway track running alongside the far end of the field. When Eric had adjusted the hoe and linked on the tracing chains to Blossom, he said, 'Lead 'er in a straight line between rows and wen yer gits to top of row, tik a fairly wide turn and bring her round to the next row,' and to Rose he said, 'yer can push hoe.' Standing there looking quite important, puffing on his Woodbine, which by now was only a brown stub, he smiled, showing a lovely row of yellow and brown teeth. He slapped Blossom affectionately on the rump, then off he went with his repartee of wind.

We were steadily going up the first row and Rose seemed happier not having to handle Blossom, when a voice called out, 'Hey, stop!' On looking back it was Windy Eric at the gate, frantically waving his arms, beckoning for one of us to go over to him.

Knowing full well that Rose would not be left with Blossom, I said, 'You go and see what he wants.'

'Do I have to?' was her reply.

'Well,' I said, 'hold on to the lines here and I will go over.'

'You hang on there!' was her answer, 'I'll go!'

Returning, she said, 'the old fart said to make sure yow 'as the horse facing the railway track when a train's coming, for if you 'as its arse end facing track, yow will 'ave trouble, cos it will bolt!'

Oh God, I thought, it's *going to be one of those days.*

'Well Rose,' I replied, 'did he say what time the trains come up the line so we can be prepared?'

'Yeah,' said Rose, 'he said "rely on yer ears", and with that he went thumping off.'

I stood looking at Rose, then stamping my foot I said, 'Hell and blast it!'

Rose's face was a picture. With a wicked grin she said, 'Eve! Yow swore. If yow's not careful yow'll corrupt me.' I had to laugh, thinking as we plodded up the row.

Oh, why does it always happen to me?' I began to dream. I could do a course in tractor driving. Then on looking back at Rose puffing and blowing I thought, *How boring, this is much more fun!'*

For three days I rather enjoyed working with Blossom, even got the hang of putting on the girth and belly strap. Rose also lost some of her fears and occasionally took a turn in leading Blossom, and every day we rode back to the stables on her back with Rose hanging on to me around the waist, squeezing my ribs so hard I could barely breathe. Blossom would get fed up with all this fidgeting around on her back that she would just stop and lower her head and we would slip gently off. She always chose the grassy ditch so we had a soft landing. I think it was her way of saying "enough is enough" for it was with great difficulty that we got her going again, so at times we had to lead her back to the farm.

We had the times of the trains worked out to a fine art and always managed to have Blossom facing the track when the trains thundered past, but this particular day fate dealt us a cruel blow. We had made it to the end of the row, and on leading Blossom around into the next row an unexpected goods train went roaring through at great speed. Blossom reared up in the air and I could not hold her; it felt like my arm would come out of its socket, so I had to let her go. She frenziedly galloped all over the field with the hoe trailing behind.

After about ten minutes the field looked as if a herd of elephants had rampaged through it. My main concern was for Blossom. I ran after her praying she would not go on to the track. I shouted to Rose to run around the other side of the field so we could corner her at the far end. Poor Rose was terrified, she was rooted to the spot with fear.

My prayers were answered, Blossom came to a full stop at the hedge with the hoe entangled in some bushes. I made a quick grab for the reins, trembling from head to foot. I did my best to calm her, she was foaming at the mouth and her eyes were wild. I stroked her gently and after a while she calmed down and bent her head to chew at the grass by the hedge. I looked down at her legs, the tracing chains were entangled around her hoofs.

Oh my God, I thought, *what do I do now?*

Rose was still at the far end of the field, to call her I may frighten Blossom, so very slowly I tied her to a thick branch then bent down and prayed that she would not move while I untangled the chain. It seemed as though she knew what I wanted of her, she lifted her hoof and I was able to slip off the chain; that done and with a sigh of relief, I unhooked the hoe. Then I walked her very gently towards the gates where Rose was standing. I was still in a state of shock, and worried in case Blossom had come to some harm.

On approaching Rose I said weakly, 'Please Rose, go up to the farm and tell the farmer or Eric to come down here.'

'Bleeding 'ell! What will he say about the cabbages?' was her reply.

'To hell with the cabbages, I am anxious about Blossom!'

Finally she went, glancing back at me as though I was sending her to her doom. I leant against Blossom to await my fate.

*

Half an hour went by then the farmer pulled up in his car. On stepping out there was a look of horror on his face, his snake-like eyes narrowed as he surveyed the scene with his hands behind his back.

'Well,' he said, turning towards me, 'what 'appened?' I tried my utmost to explain to him about the goods train, but he would not listen; he just stared at his boots and muttered about his loss of cabbages for market. It was all too much for me, with frustration I buried my head in Blossom's soft warm neck and wept uncontrollably. She nuzzled me gently.

On looking up he was gone, only Eric was standing there puffing on his Woodbine, with a look of compassion on his face. He spoke, 'Don't tik on so gal, it taint worth it, it be only a few cabbages. Yer did git Blossom afore she got on track, so cum on and I'll give 'e a lift up and yer can ride her back to stable, then we will give 'er a rub down and a feed and it will be right as rain.' I asked where Rose was and he replied, 'er was sent up to field with others to pull mangels.'

'Will I be going too, Eric?' I asked.

'No,' he replied, 'Guv'nor's Missus wants ee to go ter house.'

Oh, I thought, *it is going to be my dismissal.*

Looking up at me as though he sensed my thoughts he said, 'Yer will be alright gal, the Guv'nor realised that, when he calmed down, it could 'appen to anyone. So cum on,' he said kindly, 'forget it.'

* * *

CHAPTER FOUR
Blackie and Cider Apples

F inding my new job with the animals on the farm to be very rewarding I was shadowed everywhere by Skip, the sheep dog. We became firm friends. It never ceased to amaze me the way he wove himself in and out of the Shire horses in the stable. They looked down on his antics with a superior air, tossing their heads. Rose would visit me on the rare occasions when she could skive off from the sugar beet field.

Bursting in with "The bells, the bells", her left shoulder padded out with her jumper, she staggered around with her whole body bent forward, head to one side and her tongue hanging out – Skip thought it was great fun too, so he joined in by hanging on to her dungarees at the ankle.

Eric laughed, saying, 'It be like Spring since you young gals cum. Missus says, "Eric, yer as got a spring in yer step these days", an 'er give me extra rasher of bacon this mornin'.' His weather-beaten face lit up at the thought of it, grinning from ear to ear displaying his brown and yellow teeth.

Rose jogged my elbow saying, 'Eric, candle will be snuffed out early tonight then!'

'Reckon it will,' retorted Eric, 'it be bath night. Us 'as a bath in front of fire, and us puts in oven two bricks to warm bed.'

'Bricks!' exclaimed Rose, 'where do you put them in the bed?'

'Um, let me see,' he pondered, 'where they do the most good.' He was not giving any secrets away. Smiling, he walked away, dreaming, most likely, of the newfound

33

interest his wife was showing him these days, perhaps tomorrow for breakfast alongside the rashers would be two eggs!

*

After Rose departed we had a visit from the farmer.

'Afternoon,' was his greeting, 'I 'as a nice little job for you gal,' not looking at me directly but with the usual gaze at his boots. 'I wan 'ee to tek young pony, Blackie, Eric will 'elp yer hitch 'er up to cart, then go up orchard and pick up rotten apples and pears and tick them to barn fer cider making.'

'But, but . . . I have never driven a horse and cart,' I protested.

'It be like riding a bike,' was his reply, turning on his heels and walking away.

I pleaded with Eric, 'You will help me won't you?'

'Course I will, gal, us will 'ave a practice run up lane,' he replied, 'you'll get the hang of it, tis easy as shelling peas.' I had my doubts about that . . .!

'To be honest with you Eric, I would much rather not do it.' There was a stunned silence, on his face was a look of dismay.

'Yer must, or else he'll be in 'ere like the charge of the Light Brigade,' he said. My brain was beginning to reel from the thought of it.

Following him across the yard I was wishing I was with Rose and the other girls pulling up sugar beet. In the stable, leaning against the wood rail, I tried to rationalise my thoughts.

'Yer will be fine,' Eric said, 'cum on, snap out of that worrying, yer be alright, jump up on cart and let's drive this trial run.' I did not for one moment in time share his optimism. I hung on grimly to the reins, struggling to keep the horse in a steady line.

'Hold reins loosely in yer hands gal. Jest let them slide through . . . now keep 'im steady . . . pull this way when yer's turning and shout "Whoa!" to stop . . . that be wonderful;' Eric looked at me with admiration. I have had my black moments, and regardless of Eric's faith in me I knew this was not going to be my day. 'On yer way now gal, tek it easy . . . the sky looks o'ercast, may get some snow,' he said cheerfully.

Bidding him "Cheerio" I went on my way towards the orchard and to my relief Blackie did everything I asked of him. So, on reaching the orchard I gingerly steered horse and cart through, pulling up at the trees. I jumped down; then began my task of shovelling up the rotten fruit onto the cart.

The wind was getting up, the sky was darkening and Eric's prediction of the weather forecast seemed to be accurate. I thought perhaps it would be a good idea to head back to the farm, also, the cart was half full with fruit and perhaps I would be able to make a second journey the next day.

Halfway up the lane came a flurry of snow, then a blinding snow storm raged, I was having great difficulty in seeing where I was going as visibility was nil. On turning towards the farm I saw the gate looming towards me. Pulling Blackie up sharply I was about to jump down and open the gate when a robin flew off the gate just in front of the horse. So that settled my decision and we went like a rocket straight through the gate pulling out posts in our wake like a tornado. We came to a full stop in front of the calves' pen with muck flying in all directions and the calves running scared all over the place. The snow stung my eyes and I could only focus with great difficulty.

A voice from the swirl of snow said, 'Yer 'as done well, yer's only bin 'ere a wik but yer's just about managed to wreck me farm! What the bloody 'ell are we going to do wid yer?' It was the farmer standing there through the dancing snowflakes, covered from head to foot in muck. My feelings were hostile and I thought *I would like to tell you where to put your horse and cart, but on second thoughts that would be unladylike.*

Now, would he listen to my explanation about the robin? Most unlikely, so I resigned myself and gave an apology. I bet that was the first time in his life he had been sprayed over with muck by a female. Stifling back my giggles I was thankful for the snow for it had blinded his vision.

We rounded up the calves into their pens, doing a quick count, and then we were on our way back to the stables. Deep silence reigned apart from a few grunts and groans from the farmer. Incidentally, he did not smell very sweet either, the odour matched his mood, at least the snow was a blessing, it did help to cover up what lay on his attire.

By the way, the apples and pears lay somewhere beneath muck and snow, so my whole task was a sheer waste of time. Giving him a sidelong glance all that was distinguishable was a red glow from his pipe, which he was puffing on furiously. I had the urge to laugh, but on second thoughts, I thought better of it.

On approaching the stables, Eric was standing in the doorway; walking towards us he said, 'I told 'ee it would snow.'

The farmer spluttered in reply, 'So yer be the bloody weather cock around 'ere then, 'ere you silly bugger, git this hoss in stable.'

Very humbly Eric replied, 'Right Guv'nor, right Guv'nor, right away.' I jumped down to give him a hand and I glanced at the farmer, the way he looked at me I knew exactly what it felt to be an insect for I had that awful feeling of being stamped on. He shuffled off towards the farmhouse with his wellies going "squelch squelch", his feet swimming around in the liquid muck.

Eric chipped in with, 'It be good fertiliser, it might meck 'im grow if the stench don't gas 'im first.' He lay on a pile of straw and laughed so much I thought he would blow a gasket. He lay there with tears streaming down his face, mopping them up with something that looked like a handkerchief. Having my doubts about other things it could have been used for, I went on my way.

*

There was a great stir on the farm the following morning. Parking my cycle as usual behind the stable I was met by Eric grinning from ear to ear.

'I've 'eard tell,' he whispered as though it was some great secret I was about to hear, 'that yer t'elp Fred Rockbottom t'day wid ferrits. Guv'nor don't wan 'ee anywhere near 'im t'day.

I wonder why! I thought.

* * *

CHAPTER FIVE
FERRITY FRED

'Who is Fred Rockbottom?' I asked.

' 'e be the Game Keeper,' Eric replied, 'Guv'nor says yer will not be able to wreck nothink wid 'im.'

Ferrity Fred was waiting impatiently for me in the barn. His name suited him – he was rather small in stature with weasel eyes and a thin hooked nose with thin lips which curled up at the corner as though he had a perpetual sneer. Watching me closely as I walked towards him a small scraggy dog lay at his feet surveying me with one eye.

'Cum on gal,' said Ferrity Fred, 'us ain't git all day, we've git the traps t'check. Pick up yon bag.'

Bending down to grasp the top, it began to move. Jumping back with fright I said, weakly, 'What have you got in there?'

'It be me ferrets, gal, don't tell me yer's frit of them, they be luverly little critters.'

I braced myself when he proceeded to untie the bag. Backing away, I replied, 'I will take your word for it, but you can have the pleasure of carrying it. I-If you will pass me your haversack, Mr Rockbottom,' I stammered, 'you will have a hand free then.'

'What's this wid "Mr Rockbottom"? Me name's Fred, and yours?' he asked.

'Eve,' I replied.

'Well then, now us 'as all got acquainted we'll git on our way.'

*

There was a dusting of snow on the land and the ground was frozen solid. With a heavy heart I slipped into line alongside Ferrity Fred, with the little scraggy dog still eyeing me up with suspicion.

'Do tell me,' he asked, 'did Guv'nor 'ave much on his face as well?'

I replied, 'Probably, some MAY have splashed on it.'

'Wish'd I 'ad bin there,' he retorted with a deep chuckle, 'it must 'ave bin right funny. Eric's Missus says she 'ad niver seen Eric laugh so much.'

At every opportunity the scraggy dog tried to bite my ankle. I had that awful feeling it was yet again going to be "one of those days".

Ferrity went on about how he was a sergeant in the Home Guard and what an important person he was, and puffing out his chest with pride said that if Jerry landed here he would chase him out of the village with buckshot up his backside.

Scrutinising him I said, 'Your job must be interesting.' Thankfully he forgot yesterday's episode and Eric's disabilities and explained about his traps and how many rabbits we hoped to pick up that day. Puffing out his chest again, he went on to say what an important person he was, and that he was the farmer's right hand man.

I studied him and thought that he would be in his fifties, probably about fifty three; the majority of men on the land were that age or very young lads in their early teens, for all the able bodied young men were at war. That was why we were there, to replace them until their return, that is if they had the good fortune to do so.

Then perhaps, I thought, *they may have other ideas about life after this experience away from village life.* My ideas had changed, I was more independent. I was seeing another side of life from my strict upbringing, and I had learned quite a few different words to add to my vocabulary! My parents did not approve of the change in me and I am sure, by the look in their eyes, that my newfound freedom was not what they had mapped out for me.

*

'Well, 'ere we are,' Ferrity said quietly as if to himself; he turned and looked at me, 'yer bin quiet – penny for yer thoughts, gal,' he said with a deep chuckle.

At that time I was feeling rather apprehensive about my lesson in taking rabbits from the traps. Seeing the look on my face he tapped me on the shoulder, 'Don't look so worried, they won't bite yer, they're dead!' He went into great detail about how the traps worked and to be very careful that I did not step on one or else it could be "right nasty". 'This one be a gin trap,' he pointed out to me. It was horrendous, with steel jaws like sharks' teeth.

Poor rabbits, I thought.

He put a stick into it to demonstrate, it snapped, cutting the stick clean in half. I jumped back in horror. He strutted on with his shoulders heaving up and down with laughter. I kept a steady pace behind him and my eyes peeled for the traps.

'Well it be quick. I'm sure the poor old rabbit never felt a thing,' he retorted, bending down to collect yet another poor rabbit.

We stopped awhile to take refreshments, sitting on a fallen trunk of a tree. Ferrity slurped on his black coffee, the lemonade I was drinking, he said, would rot my socks. I was fascinated by the size of the sandwich he was about to devour, it was as thick as a doorstep. Clamping it between his jaws with his eyes closed, he munched away with a cascade of crumbs escaping from the corners of his mouth. The little scraggy dog drooled and watched every crumb that fell.

When the last morsel disappeared he opened his eyes, belched, and said, 'That'll stick me ribs together till dinner. Now let's git those ferrits working.'

Crouching down I watched intently as the ferrets were placed into the rabbits' hole. The little scraggy dog came into his own now, as with his tongue hanging out of the side of his mouth, eyes darting back and forth, he was awaiting his cue. Out shot one rabbit; in response to the softly hissed instructions the little dog was away like lightning, grabbing the rabbit behind the neck. With tail wagging furiously he dropped it at Ferrity's feet, then back he went on guard for the next rabbit. I was so thankful when we returned to the farm.

Ferrity's passing words were, 'Enjoy yer dinner gal, mine be bunny stew wid dumplings, and I'll swill it down wid some rhubarb wine.' So with deep content and satisfaction at his day's work, or should I say haul, he went whistling on his way with the little scraggy dog trailing behind him.

*

We were all going to a dance in the village hall that night, so I felt rather elated about that.

* * *

CHAPTER SIX
JOSIE AND DUSTY

The next day twenty new girls arrived, and two of them, Josie and Dusty, were put in our room. Josie was six feet tall in her stockinged feet, blonde, beautiful, and elegant. She had lovely manicured hands and was a mannequin in a large department store in Birmingham. For the life of me I could not picture Josie picking up spuds.

Dusty was tall too and very attractive. My, they would liven up the farmyard. They confessed that their ambitions were to marry handsome farmers.

'What a treat they are going to have,' said Rose, 'when they see Snake Eyes. Bleeding 'ell,' she said, 'we ain't met any yet, they be fat bald with big black hairs sticking out of their chests and bloody great muscles like boulders.' Josie's false eyelashes fluttered with dismay, a look of disappointment crept over her lovely face, but she lightened up when we told her there were some handsome fellas two miles down the road at the Royal Air Force station.

Old Snake Eyes, the farmer, actually raised his eyes to look at Josie, and she took advantage of this and fluttered her eyelashes at him, whereupon he blushed crimson, and his small eyes darted back and forth. Even Eric was not quite sure where to put his hands – in his trouser pockets or behind his back. He was puffing furiously on his Woodbine and popped from one foot to the other. Josie and Dusty were enjoying every moment of his discomfort.

'Well then,' he said, 'what you all waiting for? Take 'em up field and get them hoeing. Beans break um in gently.'

'Thank you Sir,' said Josie, fluttering her eyelashes wickedly. Nervously, he lowered his gaze to his boots. Even his ears went crimson.

*

At lunchtime we all went along to the local pub. Merv, the Landlord, was in fine form. Quite a ladies' man, he fell over himself to get to the bar to greet us all. His elderly customers were sat in the corner playing cribbage. They looked up, gave a throaty cough then spat simultaneously into the spittoon. Merv was leaning over towards Josie.

Well, sweet one,' he said, what can I get you?' She turned on the charm.

'One packet of your best crisps, and a shandy in a tall glass, and for Dusty a cocktail with a cherry.'

'Sorry, no cocktails,' said Merv. He was overcome by Josie's attention and was getting very hot under the collar. The glass slipped from his grasp.

A voice from the depths said, 'What the 'ell is going on?' Up went the trap door and his wife, Big Lil, appeared from down behind the bar, she screwed up her eyes at Josie, and passed her tongue over her generous lips, which Rose declared looked like a chicken's bum! She surveyed us all with an ugly stare, hands on hips. 'Well, who broke the glass?' We were silent. 'Come on, own up.'

'It was me, Lil darling,' said Merv.

'Git down cellar and fix beer kegs,' was her sharp reply. He made a quick exit down the steps pulling the trapdoor behind him. 'You Land Girls, what did you say to Merv?'

'Nothing at all,' we said, 'we only wanted a shandy.'

'Then get away from the bar and sit outside, I will bring your drinks out.'

The old men playing cribbage muttered, 'Brazen hussies!'

We left the bar which smelled of musty perspiration overlaid with big Lil's "Ashes of Roses".

*

Back at the bean field we all got on with the task in hand before the farmer came on the scene. At the far gate a group of Monks from the nearby monastery were standing beckoning for us to go over. Rose and Josie went to see what they wanted. Nearing the gate they were aghast at what they did. In unison they lifted their habits and flashed!

'Dirty old monks!' said Rose, Josie picked up her hoe in the air and ran after them yelling, 'You are for the chop!' They lifted up their habits and fled towards the monastery. We had certainly stirred up the inhabitants of this village.

'Bleeding 'ell,' said Rose, 'them Holy men, I would not want to be blessed by them, wait 'til I tell me ma'.'

We complained to Snake Eyes, but he dismissed it saying, 'You girls have vivid imaginations.'

The bean field was getting quite interesting, that day we had a visit from the Yanks who pulled up in their jeep and gave us chocolate, tinned pineapple and Lucky Strike cigarettes, saying they had heard back home that we were starving in Britain. We accepted their gifts, they were perfect gentlemen. Not like the Monks with their dirty habits!

The Yanks visited us regularly until Snake Eyes got wind of it and then we were sent to the far field near the farmyard, to cut kale for the cattle. It grew so tall that it towered above our heads, and when it had rained we would get drenched at the end of each row. We had to wring out our shirts and socks and empty wellies which were squelching. Josie and Dusty were all for telling him where to stick his kale and Josie wept for her lost nails.

'Sod it all,' we said. Rose exclaimed that she was off back to Brum.

I thought, *Oh, I was just getting to like that bean field, an' all.'*

*

A week later we were all separated. My first job was to drive the lorry steadily along the field as the farm hands loaded up the bales. No question of whether you had passed a driving test. It was "get in there, clutch here, brake there, just keep her steady". Next job was helping to build a straw rick.

Then I had the task of taking the young mare, Polly, to the blacksmith's for shoeing. For this I had to ride Polly, the smithy's was 5 miles away. I was doing quite well until we neared a field where a stallion was grazing. Polly decided if she parted company with me she could gallop off into the field with him. So she tossed me off and I ended up hanging on for dear life to the reins. The ditch was full of water and I was literally dragged out by Polly in her effort to shake me off, but I hung in there, dug my heels in the soft ground, and pulled her in towards a gate so I could mount. There is not a lot to grasp when you are riding bare backed. We set off at a gallop past the field and the stallion. My God, Snake Eyes had a lot to answer for! Was he in some way trying to get rid of me? With determination I carried on, I had to win.

We were going well along the lanes but it was when we hit the main road and a convoy of GIs in their army trucks roared past shouting "ride her cowgirl" and tooting their horns that Polly went berserk. She reared in the air and I slid to the ground, still again hanging on there but this time on my feet. I pulled on her reins, God, I must not let her escape. Visions of the farmer ranting came before me.

The blood from her mouth trickled warmly down my arm where the bit in her mouth was pressing. She went round and round in the middle of the road for about 15 minutes, although it seemed forever. I turned her round again towards the blacksmith's, but this time I led her, taking no more chances in case I was thrown again. I did not fancy being laid out in front of an on-coming vehicle.

On arrival at the blacksmith's it was lunch time. It had taken me three hours to get there. Harry, the blacksmith, was a jolly little man and he chuckled when I related details of our trip there. He said, 'Lead her in here. We will tie her to a ring just in case we have any hanky panky. The old bugger of a farmer you work for is a first class arsehole for sending you here with this hoss. She's been stabled all winter, full of oats, no wonder 'er's lively. Off you go gal, get something to eat and drink. Knock on door of kitchen, Missus will give you som'at to digest,' he said, muttering as he went "bloody arsehole".

Alice, his wife, let me wash the blood from my arms and brush the caked mud from my dungarees. With the aroma of burnt hoof coming from the barn where Polly was having new shoes fitted and the sound of Harry saying, 'Keep still you silly young bugger,' I relaxed. I had been given an enormous mug of cider.

Alice said, 'That will calm yer nerves gal, get it down. It will stick yer ribs together.' I was not sure about the ribs but my jangled nerves yes.

I left the blacksmith's in a calm haze, all pain gone from my overstretched arms, with Harry's parting words, 'Tell the old bugger to bring her in himself next time,' and muttering, "bloody arsehole"!

*

By the time we arrived back at the farmyard it was 4 o'clock and I had left at 9.30. Snake Eyes was strutting around with a face like thunder.

'Where the bleeding 'ell have you bin?' he stormed. In my alcoholic state I wanted to say "there and back to see how far it is"! He went ranting on about Land Girls in general and why did he deserve to be saddled with us. I tried to explain what happened but it fell on stony ground. Still ranging on with his head bowed in his usual stance, and looking at his boots he said, 'What yer hanging about for? Git up stable.' Then very sarcastically, 'Join the other members of the gang in kale field.' I wanted to mutter Harry's passing words – "old arsehole".

*

The next day we were all going away for the weekend – we had been invited to Bristol to Meg's home. Also that evening, Rose was meeting her boyfriend, Wiggins, who was stationed nearby at the RAF station. I was going on a blind date to meet his pal Tom, who was in the same air crew as Wiggins. Something pleasant to look forward to after this disastrous day.

* * *

CHAPTER SEVEN
BEAN FIELD and YANKS

It was a blazing hot August day and we were in a field picking runner beans. By midday, the heat was unbearable beating down on our backs. I could feel my back getting more and more uncomfortable and could feel the searing heat through my thin shirt. Rose remarked that a pair of shorts would not go amiss in this heat. We did the next best thing and rolled up our dungarees above our knees. There was no shade apart from the hedgerow. Rose half laid underneath the hedge feeling pretty sick from sunstroke. She was shivering and in quite a state. Josie had blisters on her lips. Madge and Dusty went to the farmyard for help. They came back in the lorry with Snake Eyes.

'Well, well,' he said, 'what's up?' Looking down at Rose he remarked very sarcastically, 'What's brought this on then, somat you have eaten, hey?'

We lifted Rose up, she staggered to her feet looking dazed and still shivering uncontrollably. He gestured for us to put her in the lorry. It was just as well that she was oblivious to what was going on because Snake Eyes would have received the sharp end of her tongue.

We tried to explain that it was too hot for us to work and asked if it would be possible to go up to the farmyard and perhaps help Ernie in the stables. He just grunted, looked down at his boots, calmly hopped up into the lorry and drove away. We stood there dumbfounded.

We decided enough was enough and we searched the next field for shade. We came across an old dilapidated tractor shed and took shelter in there for the rest of the afternoon. Madge was worried in case Snake Eyes returned and found us all skiving off, but we were past caring. My back was burning and I had a thumping headache. Josie was suffering badly, more blisters had appeared on her face and her eyes were gradually disappearing. We knew it was impossible to return to the hostel because strict rules were that no-one was allowed in until the earliest at 5.30. So we just had to sit it out until then.

Josie was all for going sick the next day, she would visit the doctor to be signed off. 'Well,' she said, 'when the doc claps eyes on me in my ugly state he will say "instant discharge on the grounds that this young girl is allergic to land work". Now Eve, what's your excuse?'

'I think it will have to be, "Come home, Gran's died"!'

'How many funerals is that now to date?' Josie joked.

Josie was signed off sick for two weeks. Rose was away for seven days and Madge and I managed to get three days off. Dusty had a sudden bout of toothache and was sent home to visit the dentist for a suspected wisdom tooth abscess.

When we returned to the farm, Snake Eyes remarked in his usual contemptuous manner, with his eyes fixed firmly on his boots, 'You young gals will have to toughen up, can't 'ave yer taking off every time we have a heat wave. There be straw hats for yer to wear in office. So for God's sake put them on and let's have no more flaking out in field.' He went on, 'Make sure you take plenty to drink.'

Rose muttered under her breath, 'Bleeding 'ell, what does the old sod think we are, his coolies?' We tried our utmost to get out of hoeing the beans but he was not having any. We just had to go back to the field, not only did we suffer the sunburn but also were bitten alive by the harvest bugs. We dabbed so much vinegar on our bites that we smelled like a fish and chip shop.

Rose and I were sent the next day to do horse hoeing. I do not know which of the two evils was the better, the beans or this. The ground was hard baked from the sun and it was murder on our feet. I sat at the edge of the field and removed my thick socks, which I realised to my misfortune was the wrong thing to do. I ended up with massive blisters and to walk was agony. At the end of the day I rode on Blossom back to the stables and walked across the fields to the hostel barefoot.

Ernie shouted after me, 'The bull is in there with the cows.' But I was beyond caring, my feet hurt too much to cycle back. The bull was there at the far end of the field but he paid me no heed. Just as well because I could not have run to save my life.

*

Needless to say I was off sick for a week until my feet healed, so I escaped the beans after all. My friends were hoeing those beans for three days.

Dusty told me they had a visit from the Yanks which livened up the days. Apparently they came at lunch time and gave the girls a lift in their Jeep to Merv's pub. Rose said they had two shandies then were taken back. The Yanks then helped with the hoeing. They produced a case of canned pineapple and then opened up several cans for them to eat.

'There we were scoffing away on this pineapple when "lo and behold" who should we see making his way towards us but none other than the Lord and Master himself, striding forth up the field towards us,' said Josie. 'We all thought, *Oh hell, are we for it now?*'

She went on to say how Rose was practically choking on her pineapple when Snake Eyes approached, looked the situation over from ground level and then stabbed the earth over with his boot, 'Well, well, what have we here? he said.

One of the Yanks spoke to Snake Eyes, 'Afternoon Sir, we just dropped by to enquire the way and these young ladies of your work force kindly gave us directions to our destination, for, Sir, we were completely lost in this beautiful countryside of yours.' He moved closer to Snake Eyes, 'Come this way Sir. Hey Spike,' he shouted over his shoulder to one of his colleagues, 'go down to the Jeep and give this good man a carton of Lucky Strike.' He remarked, 'I see you are partial to a good smoke, so try these out for size.'

'My, what a charmer,' whispered Dusty. Old Snake Eyes went like a lamb, he even managed a smile and he actually dragged his gaze from his boots.

'Wily old fox,' retorted Rose.

'So what happened next?' we wanted to know.

'Well, that was it,' said Dusty, 'end of story, not a word was uttered from his lips to either of us.'

*

The next day we all had to go to West Farm to help with the sheep dipping. Oscar was there humming his tunes and springing up and down. Josie and I were at the end where the sheep went in, if you did not jump back quickly enough a fair amount of dip went over you too. When they clambered out the other side they all looked like drowned rats. Rose was having difficulty standing up, she was helping Oscar herd them into the pens, the sheep came out with such speed spraying the dip everywhere.

'Hang in there gal,' said Oscar to Rose, 'stand more to the side, we don't want to fish you out of there now, do we?'

*

The four Yanks that had visited my friends in the bean field came to the hostel that evening and they brought along more goodies. We were allowed to invite them into the common room. The one named Spike played the piano and Jessie, one of the new girls, accompanied him; they played a duet. After that they would turn up about once or twice a week. Jessie and Spike fell in love, and before he was drafted to the Far East they married. When the war was over, Jessie went to Texas to join him.

This weekend we were all going on a forces parade through the town, so for this event we had to wear full uniform. We all searched around for decent socks to wear, polished our shoes so they shone, steamed all the creases in our hats, which were in a bit of a state having lain in the back of the cupboard for months on end, and hunted around for our ties to complete the outfit. All looking very smart we set out to join the parade. It was a wonderful sight. There were Army, Navy, Air Force, ATS, WAAFS, WRENS and at the tail end Women's Land Army. We snaked our way through the town to the Cathedral. People lined the route cheering us all as we marched proudly by.

* * *

CHAPTER EIGHT
BILL THE BULL

After our lovely weekend in Bristol, we were sent to help Danny the foreman with hedging and ditching. Danny was forever saying, 'Well, lookee here, it be done this how, anyway,' so we nicknamed him "Anyway". We had to clean out the ditches which were packed with mud and head leaves and cut the hedges back.

Josie and Dusty teased him and flirted with him, and the poor man went crimson and stammered, 'L-Leave off, you girls.'

'Anyway,' Josie said, 'anyway, we don't want to anyway.' I think he was glad when we were sent next day to pull sugar beet. It rained most of the time so we were sent back to the farmyard to the barn to an exciting job of sorting potatoes. Still, at least it was not cutting kale.

I was making my way to the bucket WC facility when a shout went out, 'Bill the Bull's escaped!' Everyone dived for cover. I ran into the dreaded lav, which one only visited for a short time (the stench was unbearable), firmly put the wood peg in the latch, and peered out through the crack in the door. He was still rampaging around and the farm hands were trying to corner him, but with head down he charged.

The rain had stopped and the sun was now beating down on the corrugated roof . As I opened the door very gingerly to breathe in some fresh air Bill went charging past with pounding hoofs. *Oh hell, supposing he comes back and charges this flimsy shack?* I thought. He had now been out there, leading them a dance, for an hour, it was getting unbearable. The stench was greater now as the temperature was going up.

I sat down on the wooden seat and surveyed my temporary haven – on the wall was newspaper neatly cut into squares hanging with string on a nail. It was "take your pick", *News of the World* or *The Mail*. There was a framed picture of an angel releasing doves to the heavens. Now, why was that there, could it be for a calming influence. It sure as hell was not doing anything for me at that precise time. Next to the seat I was sitting on was another seat, and on top of it was a flap. Curiously I lifted it up and dropped it back quickly for the stench that came from the black hole was from yet another bucket. Now I pondered, whoever would sit side by side in this place, and why? Surely they wouldn't sit together to concentrate and discuss the day's events? It made one's mind boggle.

I took another peep outside – no sign of Bill the bull, or anyone else for that matter. I just had to escape from there as I could not bear it any longer. I would have to take my chances with Bill.

I was standing outside, getting ready to sprint across the yard when I felt hot breath on my legs. There he was, as large as life, pawing the ground with an evil glint in his red eyes. I was back in that shack like a rocket. Once inside I leant against the door, trembling. Oh, bloody hell, what am I going to do? No-one knows I am in here, I expect they wonder where the hell I am. It reminded me of the ditty:

> *"Oh dear what can the matter be?*
> *Two old ladies locked in the lavatory,*
> *They were there from Monday to Saturday*
> *Nobody knew they were there!"*

I wondered if I should ask Snake Eyes, when I eventually got out of there, whether there was any possibility of getting danger money!

It had gone very quiet, so I thought *Here goes.* I opened the door and did not see or hear Bill. It was all clear. The barn doors were open wide so with a bit of luck he could be back in his pen. So I ran across to the barn where they all were still sorting potatoes.

I was greeted with, 'Where the bleeding hell did you skive off to?' Apparently Bill had jumped the fence into the field with the cows and they decided to leave him there.

*

It was not my day, some pranksters had taken my cycle to pieces with a message on the handle bars, "Will give you a lift to hostel". *That's what you think,* I thought. Josie and Rose took it in turns for me to ride on the back of their cycles.

However, the problem was that I had no cycle for the next day. We were just about to set off to work when a Yank rode up the drive on a motorbike saying to me, 'Jump on the back, I'm taking you to the farm.'

'Not likely,' was my reply, 'and if you are the one who dismantled my cycle, you can jolly well put it back together again.' His excuse was that he had wanted to date me and did not know how to ask. He eventually put my cycle back together and needless to say he did not get his date and was told to get lost, or should I have said, 'On your bike Yank?'

*

We were in the sugar beet field when we all had a near escape. An RAF bomber went into a spin and crashed at the far end of the field. The bombs they were carrying exploded, uprooting trees and hedges and leaving a massive crater where it had come down in the soft earth, with the tail tip just in sight. All four crewmembers were killed. We all wept for them. We were in shock for days, it was a deep sadness.

*

Rose, Meg, Josie and I had seven days leave so we decided to go and stay in the "TOC-H" in Stratford on Avon. TOC-H was an Armed Services Association where you could stay, it had a canteen and club and did not cost the earth. We went to the theatre and cinema, and practised our skills on the river, rowing. On one occasion we nearly went into the drink, for Rose stood up to point at something that was on the riverbank. We never did find out what it was, we were too busy hanging on for dear life with the boat rocking back and forth. We had left the farm behind and thoroughly enjoyed our leave. On the Friday, we went to Birmingham and that was great fun with Rose. Josie had all the fellas chasing her. We did not want our leave to end although Rose was keen to get back to be with Wiggins and I had another date with Tom and must confess I was getting quite fond of him. Pity their leave didn't coincide with ours.

*

On our return we were quite taken aback, for to our surprise we had four Italian prisoners of war working on the farm. They were bone idle, lazy, and at any given opportunity they would down tools and slink off. They had a guard with them but he was hopeless, and spent most of his time in the farmhouse kitchen drinking tea.

One particular day they were given the task of cleaning out the cowsheds, they were filling the wheelbarrow and had to push it along a plank of wood to the dung heap. Snake Eyes came over to Rose and said, 'Go over and help those poor boys, they are having difficulties with getting the barrow up the plank. She went over very reluctantly, put her hand on the barrow handle to give one of them a push up when he let go of it and it fell over on to Rose. She was so angry the air was blue. The prisoners just walked away laughing and sat on the steps.

Seeing this Rose picked up a pitchfork of muck and retorted, 'Bleeding get on with that you Italian arsehole,' and threw it all over him! He certainly learnt a lot of English swear words that day.

When Snake Eyes came along and surveyed the situation he said, 'Well, well, looks like you girls are going to clean the sheds out.' We went along with Rose for we knew she might do something she would regret.

Dusty remarked, 'You should have stuck the pitchfork up his arse.'

*

There was a talent competition on in the village hall that night, several of the girls were going to enter and Rose was playing the piano. We were to meet our boyfriends there, I was looking forward to seeing Tom, they had been doing a lot of flying of late. It was all very secret but we guessed it was bombing raids – all very scary. We never discussed it with them, just acted like everything was normal.

The evening went well and Meg won the competition singing, *"Sing as you go and let the world go by"*. Tom was in great form and suggested that if we could get a weekend together he would like to take me to meet his parents. Rose joked about having a double wedding but I would not allow myself to think that far ahead, I was far too young to think about settling down.

'Let's get the war over,' was my reply.

*

We were getting near winter again, the trees were shedding their leaves. I was not looking forward to frosty mornings and chilblains that went with it, not forgetting the snowdrifts when everything came to a standstill except the land girls. We had to clear snow from the yard and to the fields so the cattle could walk through for milking. The mucking out of the cowsheds was another arduous task. Some of them were three foot deep and the muck was hard packed where the calves and cows had trampled it in. Dusty remarked that she was getting muscles like Popeye.

It took quite a lot of digging to reach the floor, the farmer usually left this job for the winter months. We did not see any of the Italians or German prisoners around when these sheds needed mucking out. Perhaps it happened on other farm but on ours they had it made. On our farm they fared better than we did, they were eating white bread which we never saw – we had to put up with black bread which was like chewing cardboard with hard bits in it. No doubt it was better for us, but I did not think so at the time.

It was a very cold day with a bitter north wind when Eric asked us to help him in the stables. We did not hesitate at that, helping him brush the horses and plait their tails. Pilot, Amber and Snowflake were going to be entered for the Shire horse show in the nearby county. We were allowed to take them out for a trot around the yard. Eric beckoned for me to go over to Pilot.

'Put your foot in my hands,' he said, 'hang on to the reins and jump, there you go gal.' It was more like "There you fly" for I ended up in the straw. I had three attempts and eventually made it on to Pilot's back.

Bloody hell, I thought, *how high up it is.* I had visions of Pilot taking off and galloping across the fields, with me hanging on for dear life, but I should not have had any fears for he just ambled around the yard. It was dismounting that was the problem. It was a long way from the ground.

'Slide down,' Eric said.

I had a much better idea and rode Pilot over to the five bar field gate and climbed down; much safer to mount that way too.

They looked a picture standing there proud, as though they knew they were going on show. Eric informed us that Bill the bull was being entered for the show and he too would have to be groomed.

'Any of you gals like to volunteer?' he chuckled.

'Not bloody likely!' we replied.

'I could put a good word in for yer, to the Guv'nor.'

'You dare!' said Rose, towering above him, 'and you will end up with your head in the dung heap.'

Eric backed away, 'Only joking, only joking.'

*

The Guv'nor wants you all to go beating.'

'What the bleeding 'ell is that?' said Rose.

'It will be a pheasant shoot,' remarked Eric, 'you gals will work in the front with sticks, beating the undergrowth to disturb the pheasants so they will fly up, and then the Guv'nor and his local snob gang will shoot them.'

'Oh Christ!' said Josie, 'will we have to pick them up with all the blood dripping out of their little bodies?'

'No,' replied Eric, 'the gun dogs do that.'

Well, the day dawned for us to play our part in this unpleasant task. We all had to assemble in the farmyard.

Snake Eyes and his gang were there strutting around looking important. They were handing round the wine, but not in our direction.

'We are only the bloody serfs,' said Dusty.

'Well! Come along you Land Girls.' said Snake Eyes, putting on a posh voice and with his thumbs pushed into each side of his waistcoat, strutting round like a fighting cock with his chest puffed out, red faced, flushed from the wine which needless to say had loosened his tongue too. I noted he was not taking the usual stance of looking down at his boots but was trying to stretch his neck to give himself more height, for this was HIS show and he was making the most of it.

Josie was eyeing up the opposition and flirting outrageously. Two of the snob gang (as Eric called them) sauntered over, 'My, my,' the spotty chinless wonder said, 'I am looking forward to the company of you beautiful young gals on this shoot,' with his eyes riveted on Josie.

She was enjoying every minute and fluttered her eyelashes at him saying seductively, 'Where have you been all my life?'

He stammered and stuttered with embarrassment, 'W-Well, well, well, most likely see you in the f-field.'

'Bleeding 'ell,' Rose said, 'any more "wells" and he would have fell in with the bucket!' His silent partner realised Josie was taking the rise out of them and walked away to join the rest of the guns.

We followed at the rear to collect our sticks from the barn and lead the chinless wonders on their happy expedition, with the dogs yapping at their heels. We headed for the open countryside. There were eight of us all told, six land girls and two farm labourers, Dennis and Oscar. Oscar was a little man, we towered above him. I expect he was about 5'2", and he had a very strange way of walking. He seemed to spring from one foot to the other, he had this habit of putting his hands in his trouser pockets then stretching them up. We were fascinated by his antics. While he was doing this he hummed little tunes. Rose said she had to look away in case his fly buttons shot off with all that stretching and pulling up.

Dennis was the quieter one who muttered 'Ooh' and 'aah' to everything if it was something that interested him, it was 'Ooh aah, ooh aah,' with the emphasis on the "aah". He certainly did not seem likely to set the world on fire. They both walked in front with Oscar, who we named "Spring Feet Jack", springing on his way. As we went through a field of kale, you could just see his head bobbing up and down.

'Bleeding 'ell,' Rose remarked, 'he better watch out, they might think it is a hare.' At the end of the field of kale he sat on the ground dripping wet, looking as though he had been hosed down.

Josie remarked, 'Enjoy the shower, Oscar?'

'Ooh aah, ooh aah,' Dennis muttered.

'I'll just wring me clothes out,' Oscar replied, 'you all go on, I'll catch you up.' He was still humming to himself, it sounded to me like *"Old King Cole"*. Dusty was all for having a rest. Josie thought a lager and a fag would be the order of the day.

We were relieved when the shout went out, 'All over, return to the farm.' We must have walked miles.

On our return we were all invited into the barn. The cider barrels were used as tables with white cloths draped over them. We were told to help ourselves to a drink.

'But only one mind,' said Snake Eyes, 'we don't want you tight as ticks, do we now?' looking at his boots. Josie and Dusty mingled with the snob gang, with Snake Eyes puffing away on his Woodbine, screwing up his beady eyes, strutting around and pondering what to do next, he was fuming. We all watched with great interest, eventually, with a shrug of his shoulders he walked away towards the temporary bar. Josie and Dusty were in their element.

If only I were that brave, I thought.

*

The next day was cold and the bitter chill went through you. Bellowing cattle were wandering around the yard, apparently they were preparing to drive them to West Farm. Several had ringworm and needed treatment.

Eric ran his expert eye over every cow and remarked to us, 'You've got to know what to look for – cum over 'ere gals and I will show you what to look out for.' We skirted around the cattle to where he was standing.

He expertly moved his large hands over their moving bodies, Ha, look, 'ere be two,' he said. There were two horrible rings of sores on their hides. Some had them on their faces. He went on to inform us that we could catch it.

'Bleeding 'ell,' said Rose, 'now you tell us Eric.'

'Have you any more revelations to tell us?' said Dusty, 'speak now or forever hold your peace.'

Rose, Meg, Dusty and I were chosen to drive these cattle and not forgetting Eric who was still puffing away on his Woodbine, which was only a red stump; he was moving it from one side of his mouth to the other – amazingly he did not burn his lips. Every so often he would breathe in, then sparks would cascade around his face. We had to pass the pub on the way to West Farm. Perhaps that's why wily Eric chose us, I presume he realised he was more than likely to have problems on that score with Josie nipping off to get her lager. She was so daring, and always managed to talk her way out of the situations because the men were all bewitched by her beauty. She livened the place up.

Eric told me to walk on in front of the cattle and close any gates that were open. 'Us do not want um taking off up someone's garden or rampaging in the school playground, do we now?' We were nearing the place when one cow headed for the pub. I tried to turn it around away from the pub entrance, but before I could do this it left a large cow pat on the pub step. It splattered the rest up the door. Big Lil charged out waving her broom in the air.

'You bleeding Land Girls, why did you let it shit on my step?' she ranted on. 'I just bloody well cleaned that, you get back here and clean it up, do you hear me?' I walked away muttering my apologies, 'Bleeding Land Girls,' she shouted after me.

Eric joked, 'You will have to watch out, Eve, if you visit the pub she will be gunning for you.'

Rose said, 'Stupid cow, we ain't got plugs up their arses.'

We had one more incident on the way, a young heifer decided to join the children in the school playground. It charged around, and the children were all squealing, they were quickly ushered back into the school by the teachers. The poor animal went demented as a result of all the screaming and charged recklessly into the rhododendron bushes, razing them to the ground, eventually coming to a full stop in the opening between the bike shed and the sports pavilion. Rose managed to corner it, and with luck and patience was able to get it back with the rest of the herd.

We certainly were not very popular that day. The schoolyard was a mess and looked as if a herd of elephants had rampaged through there. It had been impossible to close the gates to prevent this because they were chained back to the fence. Next day we were ordered back by Snake Eyes to clean it up. Apparently the headmistress was fuming; she told him in no uncertain terms that he should have done the job himself and not sent inexperienced young girls to do a man's job!

* * *

CHAPTER NINE
HARVEST

It was harvest time so we were all allocated our various tasks on the threshing machine. I was on the top, cutting the bindings, and Rose, Meg and Madge were at the rear where all the dust and chaff chugged out. They emerged covered in dust looking like the Black and White Minstrels. You could just about see the whites of their eyes! I had to stand with legs apart because of the vibration of the machine and be quick in catching the sheaves as they were thrown up to me to cut the string that bound them together. I also kept a wary eye on the gaping black hole in case I vanished with the corn to be chewed up and spat out at the other end.

It was, to say the least, nerve-wracking, also, my fingers were cut from the cutting of the bindings. With the rats running amok we had to tie the bottom of our dungarees because the rats had no reservations where they escaped to when the farm hands were chasing them with pitchforks.

The rough cider came around quite regularly in a bullhorn. I think the idea was to intoxicate us all so we felt no pain and worked faster. With the heat and dust you drank it down but alas, at the end of the day, we were all three sheets to the wind, weaving and falling from our cycles in fits of giggles as we made our way back to the hostel to a much needed bath and change of clothes.

After dinner we would all cycle out to a pub named "The Red Lion". They had a skittle alley there which was great fun. We usually played against the American team who would always beat us, but it was an enjoyable time trying. They were very generous and were forever passing around the chocolate, cigarettes and chewing gum. The evening usually ended with a singsong around the piano, with Rose playing.

*

The next day saw us all back at the same farm threshing. This time round I was at the back of the black monster with all the black dust belching out – God knows what this was doing to our lungs. When you blew your nose all this black stuff came out; by the end pf the day we looked and felt as if we had been sweeping chimneys. No wonder they handed around the bullhorn filled to the brim with rough cider frequently, as I mentioned before, to dull your senses no doubt, and distract your mind from your task in hand. They were also taking advantage of the situation. We were all constantly thirsty with a dry throat from all the breathing in of the dust. At the end of the day, all I wanted to do was to get back to the hostel to sink into a hot bath and wash away all the grime.

On making my way towards my cycle, I found that some bright spark had decorated it with rats – one large rat sitting upright on the saddle tied on with string, three on top of the carrier at the back and several on the wheels. A young lad who had been working alongside us was the culprit and thought it was hilarious. Rose, Meg and three of the other land girls literally dragged him over, demanded he clear the cycle of rats and wash it down – which he did under duress. We could have done without all this aggravation, we just wanted to get away from it all.

*

At last we would not be returning to this farm, that next day we were sent to help a farmer pack his apples – a more restful time apart from running the gauntlet with a gander who thought pecking us was a good game. We encountered him when going to collect water from the farmyard. The crafty gander, who we named "Hissing Fred" managed to peck us when bending over to turn on the tap. We often ended up with wet feet where we spilt the water from the shock of getting pecked on the backside.

'I'll wring his bleeding neck if he pecks me once more,' Rose vowed. She filled her dungaree pockets with apples to use for missiles to aim at him, and hid behind the cover of a shed to await his appearance. Sure enough, when one of the girls came over to collect water, she bent over and right on cue along came Hissing Fred, neck stretched out like a hose pipe ready to strike, when Rose landed him an over-arm with one of the large apples. It smacked against his neck with such force that Hissing Fred staggered back across the yard then fell in the pond. Needless to say he had met his match in Rose and never again did he peck us, just hissed at us from a safe distance.

* * *

CHAPTER TEN
CHRISTMAS

It was coming up to Christmas, we decided that on our very next weekend off we would go shopping for presents, despite not having a lot of money to spend. We decided to buy just small gifts, and anyway there was not much variety in the shops and we needed coupons for everything. I stood in a queue for an hour to buy Tom some chocolates, and when I eventually reached the counter I was only allowed four ounces. Rose told him not to eat them too fast but to savour them slowly.

*

The secretary on the farm sent a message via Eric to say "Would we all go to the barn". The farmer wanted to see us all before we left to go home for our Christmas leave. We all speculated there must be trouble afoot and I racked my brain as to what we had done, perhaps big Lil had reported us for the cow shit. Dusty said it wouldn't be that, it was too minor and it must be something big for him to summon us all up there. We all looked at Josie.

Not quietly she said, 'I am feeling optimistic, maybe he is going to give us a rise!'

'Most probably going to give us all the bloody push,' Rose declared, 'and then we will all be scattered around on different farms.' We had been together for all this time so we would have to think of a plan for it to stay that way.

We were all packed and ready to depart for our various homes to celebrate Christmas as we made our way to the barn as the secretary had requested. We were all silent, convinced that this was it. We were all smartly turned out for this occasion in our uniforms – breeches, light fawn shirt with a green tie with WLA printed on it in yellow, grey V-necked pullover, long woollen socks up to our knees, finished off with a smart jacket which I must say was ideal in the winter months for it was lined with cream flannel. We also wore our Land Army Badges, on which was a sheaf of wheat with the lettering "Women's Land Army". We did have hats which went with this outfit but they were like mounties' hats! When we were first issued with them we wore them at a jaunty angle. I had quite a lot of hair so mine just perched on top, not very glamorous. So they ended up at the back of our lockers in the hostel. In the village we were nicknamed "The Four Musketeers" – that was Rose, Josie, Dusty and me.

Josie said, 'If I walk in first and put him off, then he will start to stammer and forget to give us the big heave-ho. Or we can all go in together. After all, we are not the only ones who have been summoned, there are Meg, Hilda and that little girl Janet, who goes around with the farm labourer, Dennis, she never said anything and would have been first to know, and we all know she never keeps a secret.'

We opened the barn door; there were trestle tables laid up with mince pies, bottles of wine and cider, and part of the barn was decorated with holly. Mistletoe hung just inside the door; several of the other girls were already there and Snake Eyes came over to wish us a Merry Christmas.

'Bleeding 'ell,' muttered Rose, 'the Last Supper, hope I do not have to kiss him on the way out.'

We were ushered over to the tables and given a glass of wine. 'Save a drop,' said Snake Eyes, 'for the toast.'

'Christ!' said Josie, 'what's going on?' There was a rather prim young lady hovering in the background and I could not place her for the life of me, I was sure I had never seen her before. She had a very pleasant face, her hair pulled back in a bun which made her look older than she was. She was about 5'4" with a trim figure and the light from the overhead lamps gave a sheen to her black hair.

'Well, gather over here, bring your glass with you,' said Snake Eyes, 'I have an announcement to make.' He walked over to the mystery lady, and putting his arm around her shoulders he said, 'I want to introduce my future wife, Helen. We are to be married in the New Year!' We all raised our glasses and toasted the happy couple.

'Crafty old fox,' said Rose, with relief, knowing we would all return after Christmas. We shook hands with Helen and Snake Eyes, and made our way out to go our separate ways. Eric very kindly offered us a lift in the farm lorry. It was a bit draughty sitting in the back but better than walking.

Josie was lingering under the mistletoe but Dusty dragged her out saying, 'You've got all Christmas for that!'

*

We all met in Birmingham, after the Christmas festivities. Tom came up with Wiggins and we spent a lovely time going to the theatre. We all wished we did not have to go back but at least we would be together for a while longer.

I had given it great thought and was determined to move on eventually. I wanted more of a challenge but I was loath to put my plan into action yet for I was very fond of my friends, and also there was Tom who was getting to play an important part in my life. He was stationed just two miles from the hostel, so I was able to see him quite often when his duties permitted.

CHAPTER ELEVEN
JOSIE'S BIRTHDAY

It was Josie's Birthday, so at lunch time we made our way to Merv's pub. There was no sign of Big Lil but Merv was in fine form. Josie volunteered to buy the drinks. She was all for teasing Merv.

'Hello there girls,' said Merv, 'what's your poison?' And to Josie who was making her way to the bar he said, 'Well, sweet one, what will it be?'

Josie, with elbows on the counter, cupped her face with her hands and went into action, gazing longingly into his eyes. She said very seductively, 'Well now big boy, three lagers and a lemonade. Oh, and four bags of your special crisps. Oh, and a bottle of champagne,' she added.

'Champagne!' said Merv, taken aback by the request, 'celebrations?'

'Lovely boy,' said Josie, 'I'm twenty-one today.'

'You don't really want champagne, do you now? Because,' he added, 'we ain't got any.'

At this point we caught sight of Big Lil making her entrance through the pub yard.

'Quick,' said Rose, 'Action Stations, time to rescue Josie. I'll go and warn her that Big Lil is on the move,' she said, 'Josie may go too far with teasing Merv and we are in her bad books already, especially with the cow dung on the doorstep.'

Big Lil came in with her eyes screwed up and her lips pursed.

'Heck,' said Rose, 'here comes Chicken's Bum.'

She stopped by our table with hands on hips and looked over at Merv at the bar. He looked very flushed from his encounter with Josie. Then she looked back at us, pushed out her over-generous bust and said, 'Well, what be going on?'

Josie replied, looking up at her in all innocence, 'Going on? Nothing at all Lil. We are just having a quiet drink to celebrate my birthday.'

'Well now,' she replied sharply, 'drink up and go and celebrate somewhere else, cos there's no singing allowed in 'ere.'

'Oh go on Lil,' said Rose, 'be a sport and let us sing Happy Birthday to Josie.'

'You 'eard me,' said Big Lil to Rose, 'drink up I says and be on your way.' Looking over at Merv she said, 'Git down that cellar and stay down there, and only come up when I tells yer.'

Merv was still hovering. 'Git!' she said. Poor Merv lifted up the flap and vanished below.

The old gentlemen in the corner playing cribbage were open-mouthed taking it all in, muttering, 'Brazen hussy.' I'm not sure if they meant Big Lil or Josie.

We made our way back to the farm and made plans to go out and celebrate that evening at the Hob Nails pub. The cook had baked a cake for Josie and we had all given part of our butter and sugar ration towards it. 'After all,' we said, 'it is not every day you are 21.'

We all changed into our finery for the evening out to celebrate Josie's coming of age, and we were given a late night pass and instructions to stay together at all times, but it was going to be difficult keeping tags on Josie. Let's put it this way, we all arrived together at the pub but as the evening went on Josie went missing. Dusty went looking for her and she disappeared too. At closing time they were nowhere to be seen so we decided to head back to the hostel and hope they had done the same. Our late night pass was for 11 o'clock. We just managed to get in before they locked the door. Josie and Dusty were not in their room. By the time it struck midnight they still were not back so we crept down to the kitchens and unlocked the back door. That was our secret entrance in an emergency, but not if anyone abused the advantage. It was used on just this sort of occasion or if anyone missed the train coming back off leave.

*

Next morning there they were as bright as buttons. Apparently they had been invited to a party at the Yanks' camp and were having such a good time they completely forgot the time.

Rose said, 'I suppose it was so good you forgot to invite us!'

Dusty said, 'We knew you two wouldn't want to come, we have met two lovely guys and we have a date tonight.'

'Well, don't forget you are to be back by 10.30, because the emergency entrance will be locked!'

'Oh come off it,' replied Dusty, 'we would do it for you.'

'Hard luck,' retorted Rose, 'we are not planning any late night rendezvous yet. Anyway, we need our beauty sleep to be sparkling bright for the early rise for the farm.

*

Next day we were sent to help Oscar (spring heeled Jack) who was going to teach us how to lay a hedge. What with his springing about, I wondered if he could stay still long enough to convey this expert knowledge. *It will be fun to find out,'* we thought. Rose said he made her head spin and she often felt like getting hold of him and compelling him to be still.

Josie laughed and retorted, 'For goodness sake, don't try it, he may think you fancy him, then he will spring even higher and hum his little ditties louder.'

We met Oscar at the end of the lane where there was a thick mist over the land. The hedge was covered in lacy cobwebs, visibility nil. We just about managed to see Oscar's bobbing head. He was humming, *"There ain't no sense, sitting on the fence, all by yourself in the moonlight"*.

Rose shouted out, 'Oscar! You've got that wrong. It should be *"hedge"*.

Ooh, ah,' he chuckled.

'Has anyone SEEN a hedge?' Josie flippantly said.

'Don't 'e worry,' replied Oscar, 'it will lift soon. Oh, ah, ah.'

'This mist is not doing my hair any good,' remarked Josie.

'Well, no-one can see you anyhow,' remarked Rose, 'unless you have ideas of going to see Merv at the pub at lunchtime.'

'Pub,' retorted Oscar, 'not likely. Guv'nor's orders. No skiving off. Ooh Ahh.'

But Josie protested, 'We can't see the hedge, so how do we know how to do it?'

No reply from Oscar, just his humming, *"Run rabbit, run rabbit, run run run".*

'Bleedin' 'ell,' said Josie, 'you wouldn't miss us in this mist.' Poor Oscar, he did not know what he had let himself in for, having Josie helping him.

Gradually the mist lifted and we did manage to get some of the hedge laid. Snake Eyes came to inspect it, or should I say his boots.

Cheekily Josie walked over to him saying, 'Well, Sir, do you think that was a good effort on our part, especially being that we were not sure where the hedge was when the mist was down.'

He lifted his head, slightly, then looked back down to his boots and grunted, 'Well done.'

'Will it be alright then, Sir,' said Josie brazenly pushing her luck, 'if we go to the pub lunchtime?'

He moved his foot back and forth stabbing at the earth, taking aback by Josie's forthright manner as it had taken him unawares.

After some seconds, still stabbing the earth with his boot he replied, 'Yer can go,' then looking over at Oscar who was springing up and down behind Rose, he said, 'you go with them and get them back here no later than one thirty.'

'But, but, Guv'nor, I was going home. My Missus will have my meal ready,' retorted Oscar nervously.

'Well well,' said Snake Eyes, puffing out his chest very importantly, 'if I says go with 'em, then yer goes.' With that he sauntered off puffing furiously on his pipe.

Poor Oscar jumped from one foot to the other. We felt so sorry for him that we persuaded Josie to forego the pub and let him go home to get his meal. He said, 'Ta girls, I'll meet you outside pub at quarter to one, then we can all go in for a quick one.'

'Good on you, Spring up Oscar,' said Josie, 'it will be our shout. Now you "spring off" home Oscar and get your dinner and see the wife.'

True to his word, Oscar was outside the pub awaiting us. He had brought along the tractor and trailer. Rose joked with him, 'Well Oscar,' she said, 'do you think we may get legless?'

'Ooh, ah, ooh ah,' he replied.

*

Merv was busy down the cellar so there was no-one for Josie to banter with. Big Lil was at the bar strutting around, lips pursed as usual.

'Well Oscar,' said Big Lil, 'how's the wife?'

'Fair to middling,' replied Oscar.

'What yer doing with them gals?' she said, 'watch out for that tall blond one, she be trouble,' she said, looking over at Josie.

'Ooh ah,' said Oscar. winking at us.

The old gentlemen were still in the corner playing cribbage, 'They be part of the fixtures,' said Oscar.

'I was beginning to wonder,' I answered, 'if they live here and had taken root.'

'Not much else for them to do in these parts,' retorted Oscar.

It must have been a great shock to the inhabitants when we descended upon them. We had shaken up their lives somehow. Take Lil, she was unsure of Josie, scared in case Merv would run away with her, not realising that for Josie it was just a game; there was no threat, it was just harmless banter. I should think Merv's problem was already there long before we all came on the scene. He loved every minute of Josie's teasing – his face would light up when she came in.

*

We all piled on to the trailer and arrived back at the farm for one thirty. Ernie was waiting in the farmyard.

'The Guv'nor wants two of you chopping logs, other two in mangel field topping mangels,' he said.

We tossed for it, heads for logs, tails for mangels. Josie and I had heads.

'Good Luck,' shouted Rose from the trailer as they sped off down the lane.

Ernie demonstrated how to split the logs but alas Josie did not get the hang of it. As for me, I eventually managed to swing the axe to get a clean split through the wood. I was doing quite well until the axe head flew off and whizzed past Ernie's head. He retorted he would bring his Home Guard tin hat next time he chopped logs with me. Ernie insisted we left it to him to finish off, and thought it would be a good idea if we joined the others pulling mangels.

*

I was meeting Tom that evening, also we had been invited to join Josie and Dusty by their American boyfriends to a dance on the base. We had yet to get permission from our housekeeper, Mrs Roberts, as well as asking for a late pass. We tossed who would do the asking, it ended with me doing the honours. We were given permission only if all the other girls at the hostel could be invited too. She did not like the idea of just the three of us going, we insisted that our boyfriends would be there but she was adamant. She rang the Commanding Officer on the base and he agreed to send transport to pick us up and to return us safely back at midnight. We had strict instructions to stay together at all times.

'Bloody 'ell,' said Josie, 'this is going to be exciting, being chaperoned by all you lot.' True to his word an Army coach pulled up at 8.30 to collect us. We had arranged to meet our boyfriends at the base.

We were informed on the coach by the driver that no-one was allowed to leave the base. He had been given strict instructions by his Commanding Officer that at the end of the evening he would deliver us safely back to the hostel.

'Oh heck,' said Dusty, 'it gets worse.'

'And you young girls,' he said, 'I want you on this coach at 11.45 prompt.'

*

We enjoyed a lovely evening. Tom and I won a prize for the Tango and the Quick Step. He received a bottle of champagne and I was given a diamante bracelet with lettering on the inside *"A Gift from New York"*. Josie excelled at the Jitterbug and had all the young men queuing up to jive with her.

Much to my amazement, we all were accounted for on the coach. Josie and Dusty were on their best behaviour . . . perhaps it was something to do with their boyfriends, Elmer and Ty, being confined to camp!

We all agreed what a great night it had been. We had all been taken aback by the buffet that was laid out for us.

There was everything there, smoked salmon, chicken, roast beef, hams of every variety, even bananas (which were unheard of) and best of all, white bread rolls, not the black variety we had to eat with the bits in that tasted like cardboard, and not forgetting the gateaux, the chocolate, the peaches, strawberries, etc. We were over-awed by the amount and variety of the food. Being rationed for such a long time, and seeing Spam dished up in various disguises, it was heaven to see this spread. We were given a box of food to take back to the hostel, full of ham, beef, etc. Alice the cook was delighted and asked Jose and Dusty to invite Elmer and Ty to supper. It was the beginning of many more invitations. Things were looking up. We were given a hand of bananas, which when shared out gave us two each – I saved my two for my young brother, Jim.

*

Tom and Wiggins were waiting for us when we returned from the farm the next day. They were upset because they had heard through the grapevine that in all probability they were being posted. They had an idea it was Bedford.

Rose said optimistically, 'We can always ask for a transfer there if they do get posted.'

I replied, 'Rose, when you both marry, you will be able to have married quarters near the RAF station.'

She did not answer and said there was something I didn't understand. She said, 'Wiggins and I are going to postpone the wedding for six months.'

'But why?' I said, 'you are both so much in love, why wait?' Apparently it was Wiggins' idea, he said he did not want to rush into anything and needed the six months to sort things out. To me it sounded ominous, but Rose was quite happy to fall in with his wishes.

We were sent to a neighbouring farm to pick up potatoes behind the tractor, then to cut red cabbages and box them up ready for market. It had been raining overnight so the ground was thick with mud. You would lift up one foot then part company with the other and we spent most of our time scraping the thick mud from our gumboots. Oscar sprang along, but at a slower pace.

Rose remarked to him, 'Well Oscar, that's stopped you galloping.'

'Ooh ah,' he replied, humming *"If you were the only girl in the world"* winking cheekily at Rose.

* * *

CHAPTER TWELVE
HOPS

That next day we were picked up in a lorry by Oscar and Ernie to go to the hop fields to pick hops. It was one of those late autumn mornings thick with mist. Ernie said, 'You will find potato sacks in the back of the lorry, put those around your legs to keep some of the cold out.'

'Where we live,' said Oscar, 'you know, the cottages, well we washes under pump and by jove that was cold this mornin'. Missus says 'Dip yer 'ead under Ern, it'll wake yer up!'

Josie cried out, Come on Ernie, get going, I'm dying from hypothermia.'

'Oh heck,' said Rose, 'that's a big word for a Tuesday. You'll not last the day.'

The cold mist was like a wet blanket enclosing around us, penetrating our very being.

'Well,' Rose retorted, hope we can see perishing hops when we get there. Josie as usual was all for finding the nearest pub and skiving off. Ernie was listening intently to our moans.

'Don't worry gals, it will lift soon. Besides there ain't no pubs where we are going, the only alcohol around them parts is the barn up back of farm where there be barrels of the rough stuff.'

'You crafty old fox,' said Josie, 'bet you have sampled it.'

'Well, that'd be telling now,' said Ernie, with a chuckle.

'Will you take us to see how it's made Ernie,' added Rose, 'we don't want to sample it, do we girls, only to gain knowledge of the production of it!'

'Well, we'll see,' said Ernie.

'Ooh ah, ooh ah,' joined in Oscar, thinking no doubt it would not be a bad idea.

*

When we arrived at the hop fields my feet, I realised, had given up the ghost on me, there was no feeling, it was like walking on stumps. I sat on the side of the grass verge, removed my gumboots and tried to get life into my dead feet. The others were all following Ernie through the mist to the avenue of hops, just ghostly shapes being swallowed up in the damp air.

At last I managed to get some feeling into my cold feet and was just about to stagger off to find the rest when a shadowy figure emerged out of the mist. It was the Guv'nor (Snake Eyes). He was puffing furiously on his pipe, the red glow from the bowl was like a beacon.

'What yer doing gal here alone,' he said.

'I was just trying to get some sort of life into my feet,' I replied.

He retorted very sarcastically, 'If yer springs to it, you won't feel the cold, go on now,' he said, 'catch yer mates up and get them hops picked.' He shouted after me as I walked away, 'Good tip for yer gal, put some hay in the bottom of yer boots, it will help to keep yer feet warm.'

'Thanks, I will do that,' I replied.

We all tried the tip and sure enough it did help but our housekeeper Mrs Roberts was not very pleased for when discarding our boots in the hall there was hay everywhere.

'Crikey,' said Rose, 'we'll soon have our own haystack,' so we had orders to empty our boots outside before coming in and changing socks, for the hay got walked into the wool.

'My my,' said Alice, 'the Guv'nor has started something with his bright ideas.' Well, for as for me and several of my friends we agreed that one consolation was that we at last had warm feet so Snake Eyes went up slightly in our estimation.

*

We walked up and down the avenue of hops filling up the baskets then going on to the end of each row to empty them out into a large canvas cot. The hops we picked we noted were just put to one side. The village people who were there working alongside us had theirs weighed each time and the weight recorded on a card under their name. I went along to the foreman in charge and asked him why ours were not being recorded.

His answer was, 'You Land Girls get paid a standard wage by the Guv'nor, and the village people are paid on the weight of the hops. The heavier the hops the more money they receive, that's why.' He added, 'they come when it's misty – hops weigh heavier.'

The rows of hops were on 15ft poles supporting networks of strong wire. The vines climbed and intertwined in a deep green foliage, and the cone-shaped fruit tinged with pale yellow rustled like paper when touched. They were used for malted beverages such as beer, and were also used in some medicines. The foreman went on to tell us that you could earn one shilling a bushel if you were a good picker.

'Well, we sure as hell needed to know that!' remarked Josie, 'I am more interested in the end product.' She shouted after Oscar, 'Don't forget the conducted tour of the barn, Oscar.'

'Hey, what yer say, gal?'

'OK, the crafty old bugger's gone deaf now,' retorted Josie. Oscar sprang faster up the row humming *"Rule Britannia"* with Josie running after him shouting, 'Oscar, wait!'

*

By lunchtime the mist had lifted, after working in the thick of it all morning, to find the warmth of the sun was heaven, it was like a grey curtain had been lifted off the earth and you could see the trees and hills clearly, and peoples faces – before they were just ghostly shapes moving back and forth.

Josie had persuaded Oscar, or should I say charmed him? to take us all to see where the cider was made. We knew she was more interested in the liquid in the barrels.

Ernie said, 'When Oscar ticks yer to barn, just stand and look interested, don't ask to taste any, just keep stumm, then with a bit of luck we could come away with a bottle or two.' Looking over at Josie he said, 'You've got to use your loaf, yer don't walk in and put both feet in it, yer 'ave to take one step at a time.'

Jokingly, Josie replied, 'But I don't want to blinking well put me feet in it, I just want to taste a drop!'

Ernie threw his hands in the air and in exasperation muttered, 'Women.!'

There was a massive big press that the fruit was shovelled into, pears and apples were squashed flat by this giant machine, and the juice from the fruit went into the barrels; some of them had been there for quite a number of years so I expect the rough cider in them was potent. We were all given a small amount to taste – it was very strong. Josie was hoping to sample more, she was disappointed though. Oscar was given two bottles of the strong stuff, he said it was good for his rheumatics, at least that was his story!

*

That night I was seeing Tom; the next day he was being posted to Bedfordshire, so was Wiggins. Rose was all for following them up there. Well I explained, it's not the end of the world, we will just have to travel further to see them.

We enjoyed our day in the hop field. at least it was an experience. The next day we were in the stables with Ernie, then in the barn stringing onions.

* * *

CHAPTER THIRTEEN
BEDFORD

Rose and I decided to ask for weekend leave, to travel to Bedford to see Tom and Wiggins. We had not heard from them and Rose was beside herself with worry. We booked rooms at the YWCA in Bedford and decided to ring them when we arrived.

The train journey was a nightmare and very scary. There was an air raid and the whole carriage shuddered and the lights went out. 'Oh God,' I thought, 'they are going to bomb the train.'

The guard walked through shouting, 'Keep calm, don't panic, stay in your compartments and keep the blinds down.'

'Bleedin' 'ell,' said Rose, 'we have no light in here so the blinds won't make any difference. There's more light out there with the searchlights scanning the sky.'

We looked out, the sky was a deep red from the bombing, 'God, some poor souls are suffering,' said an elderly lady sitting in the far corner praying, holding her rosary beads tightly in her hands.

'Oh God,' I thought, 'I hope it's not Bedford that's being bombed.' I was beginning to wish I had not set forth on this journey.

On arrival at the station, we did not know what lay ahead but thank God it was all normal. We quickly made our way to the YWCA. We rang the RAF station to let our boyfriends know we were nearby but the message was that they had gone to visit us in Stratford. We had passed "like ships in the night"! We made the best of it and stayed overnight, then travelled back to the hostel living in hope that we would see them before they returned, but it was not to be. They had already left leaving a message:

> "Missed you both, do let us know in future what you are up to. Much love, Wiggins and Tom".

*

Josie and Dusty were getting quite serious with their Yanks. We had not visited Merv's pub for a while and I mentioned this to Josie.

'Oh, we can't have that,' said Josie, 'poor Merv, he'll think we have gone off him, let's pop in there at lunch time.'

Merv was standing at the bar with Big Lil.

'Oh, that's torn it,' said Rose, 'no chatting up today Josie.' We sat in the far corner discussing what we were going to drink, then Merv came over.

'Well well, gals, we are delighted to see you. Where have you been?' And to Josie, 'Well sweet one, where have you been hiding?'

'Oh, here and there,' said Josie, winking at him.

'What's he after?' quips Rose.

Strange, we thought, *Big Lil not batting an eyelid, and instead of the chicken bum lips, a wide smile. Something's afoot,* I thought.

Merv went to the bar and said to Lil, 'Three shandies for the girls, on the house.' We were getting more and more puzzled. 'Well,' he said, looking over at Josie giving a forced laugh, 'how's the Yankee boyfriend?'

'Fine,' said Josie, 'why?'

'Well, er, er, Lil and I wondered if you and Dusty would like to come to supper and bring the boyfriends.'

'Supper!' said Josie, 'not sure about that Merv, why are you inviting us? Are you thinking of emigrating to the States after the war Merv?' she joked.

'N-No, no, nothing like that,' he stammered, 'we thought your Yanks may help us out on the drink line. It wasn't my idea,' he nervously declared, 'Lil said she had 'eard in the village that they were very generous to you up the hostel.'

'Well now,' retorted Josie, 'tell Lil that her information is not correct. Besides, it would be criminal.' He blushed with embarrassment and scurried back behind the bar.

Rose said, 'Crafty old moo, that Lil.'

Rose shouted over to Lil as we were leaving, 'Thanks for the shandies,'

Josie said to Merv, 'See you around, big boy.'

*

Ernie was outside with the tractor and trailer. 'Come on gals, jump on trailer. We are off to far field cutting kale, Guv'nor's orders.'

'Oh bloody 'ell Ernie,' said Rose, 'I hate cutting kale, it is so boring.' She jumped onto the trailer with a sigh, her voice went quiet, 'It's six days since I have seen him, I miss him so,' she brushed away a tear, 'I'm sorry for being miserable, but I can't help thinking what a lot of time we waste away from each other, why the hell is there a war? Life is for living; we sure as hell are not here on a rehearsal, we only get one bite at the cherry,' she said.

'Bloody hell, Rose,' Josie said, 'we will all end up in tears soon, come on, let's have a sing-song.'

Josie let forth with *"Roll out the barrel"*, Ernie joined in.

'I'm sure they will think we have had one too many at Merv's,' I said.

We did our stint in the kale field, it was dry for a change so we did not have to empty the water from our boots at he end of each row.

*

Two weeks later Tom and Wiggins had three days leave which by luck coincided with the weekend. We all went to Birmingham and while we were there we went to the cinema with the intention of seeing *Gone with the Wind*. We spent silent hours in the air raid shelters when the sirens went. We did eventually managed to see half the film. The Germans had been bombing Coventry solidly for days, it was devastating. The sky was red from the flames and then there was the booming of the guns.

We made our way to the station, Rose and I had three hours to spare so we went to see Tom and Wiggins off then we were going to Rose's home for a while before making our way back to the hostel. Perhaps one day we would be able to see the other half of *Gone with the Wind*.

* * *

CHAPTER FOURTEEN
HORSES AND CHICKENS

The next day we were sent to a neighbouring farm to help out there, for the farmer was short-handed owing to the fact that two of his Land Girls were sick. We walked along a well-trodden path to the farmhouse. Waiting for us at the gate was the farmer.

'Mornin' gals,' he said, touching his cap; he was a rather overweight jolly man, rosy cheeked and would not have been out of place as Santa Claus. 'Just a tick gals, whilst I light me up a ciggie.'

Carefully he charged a piece of cigarette paper with a pinch from his tin, smoothing it level with a gnarled finger, slowly, delicately he rolled it, raised it to his mouth, licked the gummed edge and placed the cigarette between his lips, then patted his pockets for the matches. He struck one match, then another, finally the cigarette burned to his satisfaction.

'Well, let's get up to yard and see what wants doing, which one of yer can drive a tractor?' he said.

'Well,' I replied, 'I have driven one once or twice but I would not like to say I was qualified.'

'That'll do me,' he said, 'yer can hitch up tractor and tek chicken food up to field and feed chickens. There be two hundred of 'em so you will need some help, so tek a mate with yer, and whilst you're there,' he said, 'collect eggs, yer find baskets in barn.'

Rose said she would take a chance with my driving. Josie and Dusty were given a job feeding the calves and cleaning the cowsheds out.

We could not believe our eyes, in the farmyard scratching around in the dirt were chickens in woollen jackets, red, green, yellow.

Rose said to the farmer, 'Why have you kitted them out in woollies, do they feel the cold or are they your pets?'

'No, no, gal. They 'ave lost their feathers, they have moulted, poor little critters, they were shivering, so the Missus knitted them woolly jackets.'

'But why all the colours?' I asked.

'That were wool the Missus had left over from knitting for the kids,' he replied. They really did look a funny sight in their outfits.

The chickens in the far field, needless to say, had still got their feathers. We were collecting the eggs, I had two buckets of grain preparing to fill the chicken troughs in the sheds when there was this thundering sound, the ground vibrated, then from over the horizon about fifty horses (at a guess) appeared apparently from nowhere.

Rose was still hanging on to a large basket of eggs, 'Bleedin' 'ell,' she screamed. She dropped the basket; the eggs crashed to the ground, the front of her dungarees were a bright yellow as the contents of the eggs cascaded down her legs into her gumboots. She was shaking with fear, come to that my legs were like jelly too, I was doubtful that I could move.

The horses circled around us, coming in closer until we were trapped in the circle. They kept pushing us with their heads until we were smack bang against the tractor. I tried waving my arms and shouting, "Back, back" but to no avail.

Rose was in a state of shock. In my hands I still held two buckets of grain. Then they decided to close in on me, nuzzling the buckets. Through my fear it dawned on me they were after the grain so I put the buckets down and just about managed to bend and scoop handfuls of the stuff and scattered it around. With that they retreated back after the grain, I distributed some from the other bucket too. Then, still trembling, I helped Rose on to the trailer and quickly I climbed into the tractor and drove back to the farmyard.

We sent Rose back to the hostel, telling the farmer she was unwell. We were too scared to tell him about the eggs and the horses, also that the chickens did not get fed. I think it was because we did not want to appear a failure, also the report that would be sent back to Snake Eyes. After a while we realised how silly that was, and after two days the farmer said he could not understand why the egg yield had gone down dramatically. We had to come clean.

'Those damned horses,' he said, 'are a bloody nuisance. You silly young girls, you should have belted them one.'

'How could we do that?' I said, 'there were too many.'

He replied that it was the rattle of the buckets that they heard, he went on, 'You will just have to make sure you do not rattle them next time.'

Rose said, 'There won't be a next time unless you have rubber buckets, and personally, Guv'nor, you can count me out. I'll stay in the yard; it's put me off horses for life, and I have never been over keen on them anyhow,' she added.

I went again, but this time with one of the farm labourers named Jack. He was a rather tall gangly man, with a thin bony face, dark Dago moustache and he spoke very slowly, so slowly you thought he was going to drop off anytime now. It was with desperation I wanted to finish his sentences. He confided in me (very slowly) that he had been engaged for sixteen years. I can understand why, I thought by the time he had got around to popping the question the long suffering girlfriend had nodded off!

On reaching the chicken pens he said, very slowly, 'I think I can 'ear 'em coming. Let's be quick with grain then they will not bother us. We leave eggs to last.'

It worked, the horses came but not seeing any food were uninterested and sauntered off to graze nearby, except for one small inquisitive pony who came behind me while I was standing waiting for Jack to collect the eggs. He nuzzled my neck and I stroked his forehead, it was then that he nipped me on the shoulder. I felt his teeth pinch into my flesh.

I shrieked out, 'Jack, help me, I have been bitten!'

He came towards me with disbelief on his face. 'Bitten?' he said, 'by what?'

'Bloody horse,' I said angrily, 'it has just bitten me on the shoulder.' My shirt sleeve was matted with blood and with that I hopped onto the tractor and took myself back to the farmyard.

'Hey,' he shouted, 'wait for me.'

'*Oh hell,* I thought, *if I had to wait for him I could bleed to death!*

The farmer rushed me to the local hospital, but it was nothing too serious, just broken skin in three places. It was very sore for a few days. I did not take any more chances with the horses and did not fancy running the gauntlet.

Rose said, jokingly, 'He may come back for a second helping!'

We spent the rest of the time plucking chickens in the barn. Josie had a goose to pluck, and with all those feathers she was covered from head to foot in white down. Our fingers were sore by the time we had finished, Josie said what nails she had once possessed were now nil, she was discussing with Dusty about going to town at the weekend to buy some false ones, and she said she felt undressed without them.

I was sent to the orchard to pick up the prunings left there. This I did with a buck rake on the back of the tractor, reversing the tractor up the rows, the horizontal metal prong of the buck rake gathered the prunings into several heaps and these were carted off to be burned by Josie and Dusty. Several times I wrapped the buck rake around some of the trees but did not do any serious damage; at least I had warned the farmer that I was not qualified.

We were only going to stay at this farm for three days but we spent a week there. The farmer said he would like to keep us there but we had to go back because we were under contract to Snake Eyes. The farmer came over to me and said, 'If I am short-handed again I will definitely ask for you, good all-rounder that you are gal,' and even the Guv'nor complimented us on our good work on his friend's farm.

*

We had been invited to a dance at the RAF station in the Sergeants' Mess that Saturday night. I had managed to save enough coupons to buy a new dress. It was blue taffeta and I thought I was the bees knees in it. I borrowed a pair of high-heeled court shoes from Dusty. I did manage to buy a pair of pure silk stockings on the black market for £1. They were sheer luxury.

Rose wore her red dress and she looked stunning with her black hair piled up on top. We each picked a white Gardenia on our way out and wore it in our hair. Dusty wore a Hungarian skirt and blouse, and with her brown hair and dark eyes she also looked stunning.

We did not always dress up like this but we agreed that we wanted to look and feel feminine and chic. The airmen in the mess were mostly Scottish so we were introduced to a lot of Scottish dancing. I was taught to do the sword dance and had to discard my high heels for that. Rose was missing her boyfriend and so was I missing Tom, so this night was a tonic to us all. Josie was being taught how to play the bagpipes and it was hilarious to see her doing the highland fling in the very tight dress that had very little room for movement.

Rose remarked, 'She'll be bursting out any minute now.'

*

Next day we were back down to earth and the mangel field. After that it was on to sugar beet to stack into round piles and cover up with the leaves we had chopped off. After lunch we went with Oscar in the lorry to collect bales of straw for the cowsheds. Oscar was humming *"Rule Britannia"*.

'Oh heck Oscar,' said Josie, 'you are patriotic today.'

'Ooh, ah, ooh ah,' he replied.

* * *

CHAPTER FIFTEEN
PIGS

That Monday morning we were given the job of feeding the pigs. Well I suppose it was a bit more interesting than cutting kale or being in the mangel field. Ernie came with us for a short time. First of all we had to boil potatoes up in this old boiler, which was situated in a brick outhouse, but before we could do this we had to light the perishing thing.

Ernie sent us into the orchard looking for dry kindling wood. Rose was nominated to chief stoker and I was her deputy. Josie and Dusty were the potato shovelers. Ernie was busy cleaning out the sties and he was welcome; the smell was vile and suffocating. Rose said it was good for the sinuses – I had my doubts about that. I just practised holding my breath when I went near the sties.

Ernie was flinging the pig muck over his shoulder onto a high steaming heap outside the sty. Every time we lit the boiler it would flare up then die down. After several unsuccessful attempts Ernie came to the rescue and he laid it with dry straw then some of the twigs we had collected, and it then roared away.

'It 'as to 'ave body in it,' said Ernie.

'Well,' said Josie, 'now we know how to light a boiler.'

'When you gits married, you gals,' said Ernie, 'you'll be able to light yer fire in the morning.'

'Not bloody likely,' said Josie, 'I'm marrying a rich man.'

The air was thick with steam in the outhouse, Josie and Dusty were complaining about their hair as the steam was taking all the curl out. We ladled out the cooked steaming potatoes into buckets, then with the help of Ernie we fed the pigs. That was an enlightenment because it was with great difficulty that we stayed on our feet, owing to the slimy muck-laden floor. They seemed to chuck it in one end and shoot it out at great speed the other.

'Yer niver sees a constipated pig!' I am sure if we had slipped up they would have eaten us for breakfast!'

'Bleeding 'ell,' said Rose, 'that fat one is attacking my gumboot.'

'Give it a quick kick,' said Ernie.

'Not likely,' said Rose, 'I may end up on my arse in the muck!'

They demolished the steaming potatoes in record time.

'Cor, they must have cast iron throats,' said Dusty, 'that will sure as hell clear their clinkers.'

'Clinkers?' remarked Rose, 'don't see any of them, it don't get time to get clinkered.'

Oscar walked up the path pushing his cycle. Tied to the crossbar was a spade, it was worn but well polished. He was dressed as usual in his old faded blue overalls, the legs of his trousers were held tightly with bicycle clips.

'Well, what yer doing 'ere Oscar?' said Ernie jokingly, 'you'll get that spade dusty 'ere.'

'Ooh ah, ooh ah,' was his reply. 'I've brought my spade 'cause I've got to dig a trench at end of field to tip rubbish in, then bury it. Guv'nor's orders,' he said, springing up and down humming, *"It ain't no sense sitting on the fence all by yourself in the moonlight"*.

He had been digging for a while then he shouted us over, 'Cum and see this,' and with his finger he delicately removed the loose earth and exposed the entrance to a tunnel, 'put your hand in very carefully gal,' he said to Rose, 'can yer feel the two tunnels? This one coming up from over there, and that one going back down away over the other side?'

'Yes I can,' said Rose.

'Oh,' said Oscar, 'that'll be where us puts trap.'

Rose shrieked, 'Trap?' and withdrew her hand quickly. 'Trap?' she repeated, 'what for?'

'To catch mole, gal,' was the reply. He pulled out a trap from his haversack, delicately set it, placing it in the hole, then carefully covered it in long grass and soil. 'Come back in an hour,' he said, 'and us will have Old Mole.' Rubbing his hands together he sprang up and down humming, *"Run, rabbit . . ."*

'You've got it wrong Oscar,' said Josie, it should be *"Run mole, run mole, run, run, run!"*

We did not go over to witness the demise of poor Old Mole. I always thought of them as fascinating creatures but to the farmer they were pests. They just kept on tunnelling, uprooting and killing plants, and leaving a pile of earth behind them They would tunnel haphazardly across the land in their greedy blind underground search for worms.

'Guv'nor says we got to start on pruning soon,' informed Ernie, 'he wants this four acre orchard done first.' We protested that we did not know how it was done. 'Well,' he said, 'we'll have a lesson then. We don't want you gals scaling the trees now, do we?'

Josie asked if we could slip off to Merv's for a shandy when we had cleaned up from the pigs. 'Come on then,' said Ernie, 'let's put our backs into it and I'll give yer all a lift on the trailer.'

*

Merv was helping to roll the beer barrels down to the cellar when we got there, his eyes lit up at the sight of Josie.

'Hello there lovely boy,' quipped Josie, 'looks like you had your Scotch porridge oats this morning. My, those muscles!' She teased poor Merv who was overcome and nearly fell down the cellar with the barrel he was rolling. Big Lil was busy fluttering her eyelashes at two American soldiers who she was listening to very intently at the bar.

'Perhaps,' I said to Rose, 'she is going to invite them to supper!'

We sent Josie to buy the shandies. Their attention swiftly turned to her, like a magnet.

'Well now Honeybunch,' said the tall one with the large nose, 'where have you been all my life?'

Big Lil was getting very agitated, screwed up her lips, tossed her head, pushed out her bosom, moved the glasses up and down the bar and strutted towards Josie saying angrily with hands on hips, 'Well? What do you want?'

'Four shandies please,' replied Josie. Big Lil practically threw the shandies, they slopped all over the tray.

'Hang in there,' said the tall Yank, 'at your service honey!' He retrieved the tray from Josie's hands.

God, I thought, *she will blow a gasket any minute now!*

They introduced themselves, the tall one with the large nose was Pope, his friend Paul. Pope said his nickname was Snozzle. They wanted us to take them back to the farm.

'You must be joking,' said Rose, 'old Snake Eyes would have a fit.'

'Let's all get out of here,' they said, 'we could find another pub anywhere away from the man-eater,' gesturing towards Big Lil who was crashing around behind the bar, her small narrow eyes screwed up.

'No thanks,' we chimed, dragging Josie with us. We were thankful that Ernie pulled up in the yard with the tractor and trailer.

The Yanks jumped in their jeep calling out, 'See you later Honeys.'

'Cum on,' said Ernie, 'let's get you all safely back to the farm.'

'Shame,' said Dusty, 'I did fancy a ride in that jeep.'

'Just as well I came along then, weren't it? said Ernie, 'or else Guv'nor would have had my guts for garters if one of you had gone missing.'

* * *

100

CHAPTER SIXTEEN
IT ALL BEGAN WITH DAISY

I moved on to do a course in dairy farming and tractor driving and my stay at the farm was to be for six months where I would be billeted in a village with three other girls. It was sad to leave my friends, especially Rose, but with luck she would be joining me in two months time, to work on the same farm where I was to train, but would be billeted in the nearby hostel.

On arriving at the farm, the farmer was the exact opposite of Snake Eyes. He was a gentleman, his wife and family were lovely, and I knew that I was going to be happy there.

I was introduced to Marjorie, one of the girls who I would be billeted with; in civilian life she worked in the Foreign Office – we all came from different walks of life.

I waited outside the farmhouse office in the summer sun. It was baking hot, the chickens were scratching around in the dirt and dust and the sheep dog was lying on the cool step in the shade looking at me with one eye, summing me up no doubt. I was ushered into the house by Marjorie, to sit with the family while they discussed the day's tasks, also which cow would be suitable for me to practise on. I was feeling rather nervous about that.

'I hope she is gentle,' I said.

Alice, the farmer's wife, was a rosy-cheeked jolly person, a rather large lady, but she was warm and pleasant. Pushing a cup of tea towards me she said, 'You are a bit skinny, are you strong enough?' Then turning to her husband she said, 'We'll give her Daisy to milk.'

'Well,' said the farmer cheerfully, 'let's get to sheds and see what we can teach you on your first day.' He passed me a milking stool and I walked towards the shed, my knees knocking.

'Well, here she is, the quietest cow, old Daisy,' he said, winking at me, 'wash your hands in barrel and we will get to it. Jack will keep an eye on you,' gesturing to a young lad of about fifteen years old who was standing at the bottom end of the shed open-mouthed, watching my every move. 'Shut your mouth Jack lad,' said the farmer, 'do it later when flies come in!'

The farmer wished me good luck saying it would be easy as riding a bike. I wished I could share his optimism. He walked down the shed talking to all the cows patiently standing in their stalls waiting to be milked, patting their rumps as he went past each one calling them by name – Patty, Hyacinth, Tulip and so on.

While the farmer was preoccupied Jack came over to me, grinning, saying, 'Need any 'elp gal, 'ave yer ever seen a diamond under a cow's belly?'

I replied, 'No, I have never had the occasion to view under a cow's belly, but let me guess, I am now going to find out.'

'Well,' he said, 'bend yer 'ead, look this it be.'

I peered under Daisy's belly and was squirted in the eye with milk. The little sod thought it was hilarious and fell about laughing. *His time will come,* I thought, as I struggled so hard to squeeze milk from Daisy's teat, the perspiration dripped from my forehead.

Then it happened. Daisy was undoubtedly so fed up with all this pulling and squeezing that she lashed out, and the stool was kicked from underneath me with such force that I went like a rocket under several cows, out the other end at the farmer's feet, covered in muck and with tears stinging my eyes.

The farmer hauled me up and said, 'Never mind girl, go wash in barrel, clean yourself off.' With that he retrieved my stool which had ended up on the other side of the shed and which had hit Jack across the back when he was milking with such force that Jack's foot shot out into his bucket, so the milk was going in a steady trickle down the shed into the drain. I felt like weeping and saying "to hell with it all" and sticking the bucket on cheeky Jack's grinning head.

I slithered towards the barrel, washed and wiped off as best I could under the circumstances, and with determination began to try again to get milk from Daisy, but kept one eye on her leg near the bucket just in case.

Then, to my delight, the quick squirt of milk went into the bucket. My fingers and arms ached but I kept at it and milked Daisy. I was so elated and pleased with my achievement with everyone praising me for sticking at it that I got carried away and was eager to please. So when I was asked to go across the yard to help Marjorie feed the calves on the other side of the yard I could not get there quickly enough. I decided to take a short cut across the yard.

No-one had thought to mention to me that it was a dung heap, hard-baked by the sun; to me it was earth. Taking three running steps it happened . . . I began to sink! The more I struggled the deeper I sank, until eventually I was up to my armpits in muck. The farmer had to drag me out with a pitchfork. With the suction of the muck I lost my wellies and socks, and to my embarrassment they all roared with laughter. I burst into fits of giggles too because I could see the funny side of the drama.

The farmer said it was the best laugh he had had in years and added, 'Well, gal, yer 'ave guts. Go along and see the wife and she will lend yer some of her clothes.'

When I approached the farmhouse little Sal, their daughter, was sitting on the grass in their garden making a daisy chain. Looking up at me with a startled look in those lovely blue eyes, she ran bawling, 'Ma, Ma, the new girl is covered in muck.'

Her mother stared at me in amazement and for a while did not speak, with hands on her over-generous hips, mouth wide open she had a look of disbelief in her face at what she was seeing.

When she did speak she said, 'What 'appened to yer gal?' When I explained she too roared with laughter and replied very kindly, 'Never mind dear, go in the washhouse and I'll git you a change of clothes.'

When she reappeared I was presented with a pair of jodhpurs about 38" round the waist, one shirt – bust size 42" at a guess (I was only a 32" and a 32" hip), one pair of socks (the farmer's), one pair of wellies, size 7 (I took size 5) and then she closed the door on me.

I stripped off my smelly clothes and washed in the large flat sink with a pump at the end, which shot water out in all directions. There was a large bar of Sunlight soap which kept slipping out of my hands under the sink, and when I did retrieve it, it was difficult to get a good soapy lather because the pump water was so cold. After getting rid of the last remains of muck I did smell sweeter, if it was only of Sunlight soap.

Then to dress. Alice had also given me a bra of hers, which I gave a miss, needless to say, not to sound unkind, but my bust kept popping out over the top of the enormous cups and I kept thinking that they would have fitted Daisy's udders better than mine. Then the shirt, which fitted like a sack – the sleeves I rolled up because they went past my hands. Next came the jodhpurs. I pulled them up as high as I could and on seeing some string I tied it tightly around my waist. With the excess mostly under my armpits the long baggy shirt disguised what lay beneath. So far so good.

Socks were odd and also a size 9; *Still, never mind,* I thought, *press on.* I tucked the excess under my toes and put on the wellies. They came up past my knees and my feet were lost in them. As I lifted up one foot it nearly parted company with the other, so I sat on the step and thought about what I was to do. In the corner of the washhouse was some newspaper hanging on the wall so I packed the toes and sides of the boots and tied string round them to keep them on my feet.

With trepidation I opened the door and shuffled out. I must have looked very much like a scarecrow. I walked away gingerly towards the cowsheds, feeling quite an idiot, but to my amazement they were all kind to me and said if it had happened to them they would have given up.

Then, with horror, I suddenly realised that I had left Alice's bra hanging on the pump handle. So I confided in Marjorie, and in a fit of giggles she went and retrieved it for me before the farmhands went in there to wash up the milk churns.

Later, I was invited into the house for a meal and they said they were very pleased to have me working for them and that I brightened up their day. Little Sal gave me her daisy chain.

I was allowed to leave early so that I could get back to the billet before the other girls returned. On arriving back I parted company with the wellies and crept through the back entrance in my stockinged feet, or should I say odd-socked feet, and quickly fled up the stairs to my room. Then to get a much needed bath – it was heaven!

*

Next day dawned with more surprises. Jack informed me as I was parking my cycle that the Guv'nor had told him to tell me to clean the bull out. I said 'He can't be serious,' and asked if he was sending me up.

With that he said, 'Alright gal, come and see for yerself.'

So I followed him towards the pen. Lying there so peacefully was the young bull who Jack informed me was only a two-year-old and "right docile" and would not be fierce until he reached the ripe old age of four.

So I said, 'Very well.' Jack's parting words were, 'Don't forget to pull the bolt firmly across when ye have finished.'

First I thought that if I fed him when he awoke he would be fully occupied eating whilst I cleaned out his bed. With one eye on Bill, I tossed a pitchfork full of clover into his manger, saying what a lovely fella he was and begging him to stay exactly still. He started and looked at me with one eye. With that I nearly dropped the clover all over him for my whole body shook with fear. I was going to make a dash for the door but with a heavy snort he just rolled over and went back to sleep.

Still shaking I did not dare go for the barrow in case the squeaky wheels should wake him, so I threw the muck through the door onto the pit that I had had the misfortune to fall into. *So far so good,* I thought. Now I had to fill the water trough, but how would I do that, for he was lying against it? I dragged the hosepipe from the milking sheds and prayed that I could keep a steady hand and squirt the water over Bill, and with luck into the trough. Three deep breaths and I turned on the hose.

My prayers were answered, for I managed to get enough water in without a drop falling on my sleeping friend. I pulled the bolt on the pen firmly into place and breathed a sigh of relief.

I was about to walk away when the farmer came towards me and said, 'What the 'ell do ye think you're doing there gal? Who gave ye permission to go in there? – he be wild.' I told him that it was alright and that I had fed him on his instruction from Jack.

His face went purple with rage – he exploded, 'He did what?' He peered over the door at Bill who was still snoring away. 'Ye've made a good job of it gal, but you could have been killed. I'm the only one he will let into the pen – let alone clean him out! Well, well, being ye've done so well, how would ye like the job every day?'

I replied, 'No thanks.'

All I could think of at that precise moment was to get my hands on that evil Jack, but needless to say, the farmer gave him an ultimatum, 'Stop monkeying around or you will get your marching orders!'

* * *

CHAPTER SEVENTEEN
TOM AND WIGGINS

Rose received a message from her boyfriend that he thought it a good idea if they had a complete break for a few months and said something about getting things sorted out. Rose was convinced he was seeing someone else.

'More than likely,' said Josie. 'Tell him to get lost,' she added.

Things were not working out for Tom and me either, he wanted more from the relationship than I was prepared to give, but I was very fond of him and knew I would miss him if I ended it. In the war years you never really had time to get to know one another completely, it was not like you would see them every day, or even once a week, you just snatched happiness when time permitted. For how long, you were never sure. It was a case of we may not be here tomorrow!

That's why it was so painful when I had the message that he was missing. I wished that I had been warmer towards him and given him more in that limited, but oh so precious time we were together. I was devastated, it hurt so.

Rose eventually finished with Wiggins. She was fed up, she said with his messing about, it was making her a nervous wreck. She moped around for a few weeks but then was back to her bouncy self again. I now decided it was the time to move on, I just had to get away from all the memories. However, I knew I would miss my friends.

This is the last poem Tom sent to me:

My portrait lay in your eyes my love
I brushed away a tear from your dear face
When I whispered goodbye.
You will be forever in my thoughts
Even in the gentle breeze in a summer's sky.

Dearest Eve, I fly on a wing and a prayer
until we meet again.

Much love,

Tom

* * *

CHAPTER EIGHTEEN
MORGAN'S FARM

Margie and I were billeted with an elderly couple in a cottage near a dairy farm. The room we shared had two beds separated by a marble-topped washstand with decorative jug and bowl. The walls were whitewashed and bare apart from a faded picture of a Christ figure with arms out-stretched beckoning a host of children with the wording *"Suffer Little Children"*. A large heavy oak wardrobe stood against the far wall. There were no curtains to the skylight window which slanted to the eaves, so we could lie there and look at the stars or watch the clouds roll endlessly by if we were fortunate enough to get the time for that luxury. The mattresses were feather – sheer heaven – you just sank into them, but they were very difficult to rise out from on a cold frosty morning. We had to rise at 4.30 am to enable us to get to the farm for 5.30 am.

*

The grandfather clock chimed the hour, we crept down the creaking stairs in our stockinged feet so as not to wake the elderly couple. A quick cup of tea and then a cycle ride five miles to the farm with thick frost on the handlebars. Not a soul in sight as we cycled through the village, the moon still casting its eerie shadows over the land, skirting around the thick patches of ice shining in the ghostly half light.

We made our way to the farm and milking sheds. The cowshed's only light was from oil lamps which cast shadows all around. Looking along the row of cows waiting patiently to be milked my heart sank, for they were the largest cows I had ever seen. The breed was the Blue Roan, and they were massive. I felt like making a hasty retreat.

Margie thrust a bucket and cloth into my hand saying, 'Your first task is to wash them down.'

With trepidation I approached the first cow, bent over to wash around her teats when she brought her tail round with such force it ended up around my neck. I pushed it back with my other hand – thank God there was no muck on the end of it. I mentioned this to the young lad who was trailing behind me, whose name was Percy.

His reply was, 'It be good for the complexion gal,' but his cheery banter did not stop my insides from quaking and there was nothing more I wanted at that precise time than to turn and run far away from there.

'Come on gal,' said Percy, 'cheer up, watch this.' The farmyard cats were stalking up and down, meowing. Percy squeezed the cow's teat and aimed it at the cats' open mouths. 'Come on,' he said, 'try it. Here, squeeze hard now, and aim!' By the end of the milking session I did have success and managed to shoot milk into the cats' mouths and fill the buckets as well. Dear Percy, by making fun of the situation, had helped me to overcome my fears.

After the milking, we went back to the billet for an hour and a half's break to have breakfast which Elsie, our landlady, cooked for us. Then back to the farm to feed the calves, boil the potatoes for the pigs, collect the eggs from the hen houses then get the stalls ready for the cows for milking again at three thirty. We finished at 5 o'clock, had dinner at 6.30 and then were in bed by 8 pm. Margie and I were so tired we had no energy to do anything else for we were up again the next morning for 4.30 am. I missed my friends, especially Rose. We were only allowed one long weekend a month. With dairy work you were there seven days a week, although sometimes we managed to get a

Sunday afternoon free. Dear kind Percy often stood in for me on these occasions.

*

Elsie was a kindly soul who took great care of us, nothing was too much trouble for her. She was like a rosy apple, with a round smiling face that seemed to light up when we came through the door. She always wore a wrapover apron with flowers on, and fluffy slippers with the sleeves of her blouse rolled up, and she always looked as if she was prepared to take on any task that would be dished out to her.

Her husband Ern was a bumptious little man full of his own self-importance, who knew everything. She always referred to him jokingly as "right Captain", and on walking away she would wink at us and mutter "up yours, Captain Know-All"!

I think she looked on Margie and me as her temporary family, for they had no children. When we returned in the evening she would be standing at the gate waiting for us. At first we enjoyed all this attention but then we began to feel overpowered by all the kindness. They even started to question who we were going out with and where, and to be back at a certain time when, if of an evening we did have any energy left, we would cycle off to the next village and meet up with the other girls from the hostel. Bumptious Ern insisted that we had to return by 9 o'clock sharp and said he had had orders from the farmer, or else we would never get out of bed the next morning. We thought he was taking his so-called authority too far, and it began to grate on us.

On one such occasion we went out for the evening and met up with several people we knew from the hostel and had such an enjoyable time playing table tennis at the local

YMCA that time flew by so quickly we did not notice. Margie was panicking.

'Oh God!' she said, 'we will never get back for 9.30.'

One of the land girls we were with said, 'There is a short cut across the fields, it will save you thirty minutes. Firstly you have to pass through the local cemetery, then you climb a fence into the field . . .'

'But,' I protested, 'we have our cycles.'

'Well, just lower them over to each other,' she said. 'Oh, and by the way, there could be cattle in the field, oh, and a bull may be with them!'

'That lets me out then,' I remarked, 'we will play it safe and go the road way.' Margie was so upset about being late that against my better judgement I consented to take the short cut. Sylvia, the land girl, was to be our guide to the churchyard and cemetery, then from then on we were on our own. It was pitch black and when an owl flew out of a nearby tree, we nearly passed out with fright.

'Whose bloody idea was this?' said Margie.

'Not mine!' I replied. We very nearly fell into a newly dug grave.

At last we stumbled into the fence.

'Shine your cycle lamp,' I asked Margie. 'Hell, have you seen the size of it?' she said.

'Bloody hell! Are we going to climb that?' sobbed Margie.

'Yes, you jolly well are going to, because no way am I going back now after coming this far.'

'Then you go first,' she said.

'Just pray it is not an electric fence,' I said, and just managed to get a foothold in the spaced wire. Then on reaching the top I threw my jacket over the ridge so as not to get it tangled in any loose wire that might be lurking unseen. Then I dropped down into the field.

'Right Margie,' I shouted, 'I will climb halfway up then you lower the cycles down gradually. Ready now,' I called out, 'let's have my cycle first, then yours.'

'Trust you,' she shouted back, 'to go over first, I've got all the lifting to do with these bloody bikes.'

'Well,' I shouted back, 'after all it was your idea for me to go first.' *Give me strength,* I thought.

We managed to get the bikes over but Margie let mine down with such force that my cycle lamp fell off, so we spent an age looking in the long grass for the batteries, wire and bulb, which in the dark made it near impossible. We could not see anything . . . and I had an awful feeling that we were not alone!

'Oh hell,' I said, 'let's get going slowly and pray again Margie that the bull is not in here. For God's sake, don't run, or they will stampede.' I dragged her back before she took flight. We painstakingly made our way slowly through the cattle. In the dark they were just large shapes and shadows.

We were nearly coming to the end of the field when we could just about make out a shadowy figure standing with an old oil lamp, its light was flickering back and forth creating large shadows.

'Bloody hell, what's that?' said Margie.

Jokingly, I remarked, 'I expect it is Bumptious Ern getting ready to shoot us for being late.'

114

'Oh my God!' she said, 'it is him, and he's got a gun.'

'Oh come on Marg,' I said, 'don't let your imagination run away with you, get a grip, let's hop on the bikes and head towards whoever it is. The cattle are far behind us so we are in no danger.'

'Why are you so bloody optimistic?' she asked, 'how can you joke about everything at a time like this? We are in for it, terrible trouble,' she wailed.

'Come on Margie, the worst thing that can happen to us is for us to be dismissed, and that would be a blessing in disguise,' I replied.

We neared the shadowy figure, which shouted out, 'Who goes there?' We did not answer, then the voice shouted louder, 'Halt, or I will shoot!' My mind raced, perhaps it's the farmer who thinks we are cattle rustlers. By this time Margie was having an hysterical fit.

'Don't shoot,' she screamed, 'it's m-m-m-m-m-m-m-me, M-Margie!'

'Come forward,' shouted the figure, 'and be recognised.' We cycled towards the figure who was standing with a rifle pointing directly at us. 'Dismount!' the voice commanded. 'Come forward and be recognised.' On getting closer I could see it was Bumptious Ern in his Home Guard uniform.

'For goodness sake, Ern,' I said with relief, 'put that rifle down, it is only us. What did you think we were? Germans?'

'Don't be saucy,' was his reply. 'What time do you think this is to come home? It's 10 o'clock.'

'I'm sorry, and so is Margie, but we forgot the time.'

'Well,' he retorted, 'you won't forget the time again because you will not be going out again.'

'Come off it Ern, we are grown up, we cannot be treated this way. After all, we have apologised, what more do you want?'

He ranted on, 'You will do as you are told and that is that.'

'Oh yes?' I replied, 'you and whose army?'

'Oh God!' said Margie, 'don't antagonise him any more.' I was so cross.

'How dare he treat us like this? We work hard during the day – we need some relaxation!'

*

Poor Margie was so upset I only managed to persuade her to go out once more, and that was on a Sunday afternoon. We stayed for three months at that farm. It was sad saying goodbye to Elsie, but we were both pleased to be moving on. I was eager to go before then and did think perhaps I would get Rose to send a *"Come home your Gran has died"* telegram, but stuck it out for Margie's sake, although at times it was unbearable.

CHAPTER NINETEEN
GRAN

Walking at a slow pace from the station, I wondered for a moment what there could possibly be here in this village for me, with only thirty houses and one public house and one small shop selling nothing but stamps, cigarettes and matches. Being young and full of life, I hated the place, the dreary lines of washing, the loafers by the pub walls, the gossips huddled together by their cottage gates, eyeing every stranger with suspicion. Walking on I came to the small converted farmhouse on the north side of the village. The door was open to the warm afternoon.

I called inside, 'Is anybody there?'

A woman in an apron appeared from the kitchen and said, 'Well, I suppose you be the new Land Girl. Have you had your dinner?' With a look on her face that read, "do not say no", I replied that I had eaten but may I have a drink. A look of relief spread over her thin, tight-lipped face.

Mr Pratt was the farmer's name. I wondered what Rose's comment would have been. I myself, had great difficulty voicing the name when I eventually met him, for he fitted it very well. Pratt was about 55, face small, bone structure narrow, with thin lips, sparse receding mousy grey hair, grey eyes that were rather close together. There he sat in the barn with a mug grasped in both hands, staring at the chickens scratching around in the dust. I stood for a moment before I spoke. Looking up he transfixed me with a narrow stare of surprise.

'Ahh,' he said, 'you must be new Land Gal. Did 'er mek you a cuppa tea?'

'Yes thank you Mr er, P-Pratt,' I replied. He went on guzzling his tea, then threw the dregs at the chickens who flew in all directions.

'Ain't had any 'elp since Ernie went to war, so it be you and me to run this 'ere farm. We'll see how us will git on.' I had already made up my mind not to stay any longer than possible. Perhaps my grandmother could die suddenly again! Poor Gran, she already had had three funerals but somewhere up there in heaven I felt sure she would forgive me, under the circumstances.

He staggered from the position on the orange box towards me, belching as he stretched out his back. I felt a deep rush of repugnance about Pratt. *Gran's funeral will have to be quite soon,* I thought. He insisted on taking me on a tour of the farm and proclaimed what he expected of me.

'Five thirty sharp mind, to milk cows, feed pigs, help in the dairy to separate milk, for churn lorry picks them up at 8 am' he said, 'then us 'as breakfast at half eight, mucking out after. Then I'll want yer to boil taters in the old copper house for pigs, but mind not on a Monday – that's the day 'er does the washing.' No wonder all their clothes looked grey.

"Er" was his wife Mabel. He noted the look of surprise on my face and added, 'Well! We be all in bed by eight, so you will have plenty of rest, there be nowhere to go round 'ere anyhow.'

'But there is a pub,' I said weakly.

'Young wenches don't go in pubs!' he said sharply, with a snarl on his face.

That's what you think! I thought, as we walked towards the house.

'I object strongly to being called a "wench", Mr er, P-Pratt.'

He looked at me, screwing up his ferrity eyes, explaining in his rough way, 'It only be a figure of speech, as you might say.'

*

Making my way through the garden, scarlet beans budded low down with sprays of flowers curling around the hazel sticks, swallows were flying high in the warm air above the house. Then I passed the copper house for boiling the pig potatoes, and that did the washing on Mondays, the blue and orange steeples of lupins amongst the weeds and not forgetting the bucket lav with hollyhocks growing all around it.

For the short time I was to stay there I learned the secret of the beautiful pink and white hollyhocks, which would have done any fine garden proud. Old Pratt watered them on Friday and Saturday nights as he staggered his way back from the pub. They were fertilised from the beer he had drunk. How did I know? Well I was in the lav and was under the impression it was raining until I looked through a crack in the door – Pratt was doing well, until he lost his balance and ended up "legs in the air" in a patch of stinging nettles. I suppressed my giggles and did a detour around the back, through the orchard to the house.

At breakfast the following morning he stood, leaning against the kitchen wall, to eat his. Mabel's comments were, ' 'ave yer got boil on yer arse, or could it be a splinter from orange box in barn?'

Needless to say, I did all the milking that morning because Pratt had difficulty sitting on the stool. His excuse was rheumatics. I was tempted to give him some advice to soothe his tender parts, like rubbing in a dock leaf, but thought better of it.

*

After two weeks I felt starved of an intelligent conversation, was beginning to talk like them even to the "Ahs" and "Ees". Their main topic was who had the longest beans and the size of their marrows, which was a well-planned, guarded secret until judging day at the Village Hall. Pratt always won. I knew his secret and took an instant dislike to both veg. The content of the bucket lav was his fertilizer.

Then there was the episode of the village idiot, Herbie. Apparently, as the story goes, he got inebriated on rough cider and thought a cow's horns were the handlebars of his cycle. Until this day, I cannot make head of tail of that one.

I must put my plan into action and escape – to ring Rose, for she will be sending the "Come Home – Gran" telegram. That's of course if there is a 'phone box in this God forsaken place'. I must admit I had been interested to see how the real country folk lived, but I was now desperate to get back to civilisation. *Surely the pub will have one*, so I made my way there on Mrs Pratt's cycle which was one of these "sit-up-and-beg" bikes.

At the side of the pub were the loafers, puffing away on their Woodbines. Herbie, the village idiot, had his whole body entwined around the lamppost, grinning at me with his tongue dangling helplessly from the corner of his mouth, the dribble dripping from his chin. I felt an awful feeling of repulsion, pushed the cycle and hurried on into the Den of Iniquity, pushed open the large doors – visibility was nil; the air was laden with swirls of smoke. There was a hubbub of voices, but as I made my way through the mist to the bar a silence fell. I suddenly felt ill at ease. My footsteps echoed on the hollow wooden floor. My first thought was to take flight. I looked around at my audience. They were like dreary looking waxwork figures with smoky mist lingering around them, a spittoon in the centre of the room. My confidence was beginning to leave me. The dizzying waves of whisky fumes enveloped me.

Turning on my heel, I was about to leave when a voice from the bar said, 'Hey, wait a minute gal. Yer must be old Pratt's new land girl!' It was the jolly face of the landlord that changed my mind. Then, as if by magic, everyone came back to life. I felt rooted to the spot.

'Come on gal,' he said, 'what can us do for yer?' Stuttering, I asked if I could use the "phone". He gestured for me to follow him into the parlour. 'If it be urgent like,' he said.

'Indeed it is,' I replied.

I knew full well that Rose would be in the hostel at that time of day, for she was doing a stint of "domestic" – cleaning the dorms – the punishment for telling the farmer what to do with his sugar beet. 'Right ho! Message received, over and out. Action Stations, pack bag, get ready to leave 1330 hours,' was her reply.

Thanking the landlord on my way out, he refused payment for the call and gave me an invitation to come in anytime, addressing the audience of waxwork figures he said, ' 'er would brighten the place up! Wot do yer say?'

Mumbles of 'Ooh,' or 'Ooh ar' came from the room, with the occasional "ping" in the spittoon. I made my way quickly outside, my mission accomplished. Herbie was holding the cycle for me. Smiling at him I placed into his hand a sixpence, for he must have guarded it for me from the loafers. He danced around me, then before I sat on the saddle he polished it with the sleeve of his frayed jacket. Poor Herbie. I had a feeling of guilt for that earlier feeling of repulsion towards him. He was, after all, a gentle soul.

The usual gossipers were huddled together at their gates watching my every move. I most likely would be the scarlet woman for the week. I wondered who they would choose for my lover. I dreaded to think! I was fascinated by the very large lady with the over-endowed bosom. She was doing a balancing act, first with one, then the other on top of the gate. I nearly fell off the bike and said, 'Whoops.'

She thought my remark was intended for her and called out after me, 'Cheeky Missie.'

*

Pratt was tinkering around under the tractor, so was oblivious to my return. Mabel was darting back and forth through clouds of steam, hanging out the washing. She had left my lunch on the kitchen table, covered with a saucepan lid. Helping myself to a glass of milk I sat and pondered what excuse I would give Head Office for my sudden departure from here. Perhaps I could have an allergy to cats (they did possess five), then again, that was a lame excuse.

Pratt came rushing into the kitchen covered in oil and grease and waving a spanner about in anger. The air was blue with his ranting and raving. I just calmly carried on eating my lunch. This infuriated him even more. Banging his fist on the table, the saucepan lid shot into the air and did a somersault before hitting the floor. It was just as well I had finished the milk, for the glass followed suit, sprinkling glass all over the place. Three of the cats had been sleeping peacefully curled up in the old armchair. They fled, screeching, in all directions. Looking up at him I knew now no excuse was needed.

Mustering all my strength I pushed back the chair, walked towards him with the last morsel of pork pie in my hand, my whole body trembling with fear.

I said, 'Please let me pass, Mr Pratt, the pigs need feeding.' It was the first thing that came into my head.

He stepped aside saying, 'Are yer going to feed em pork pie? He he.' I walked on to the boiler house to seek out Mabel. She tapped her foot on the tiled floor as I poured out to her the events that had gone on in the kitchen.

She brushed away strands of hair from her face which was dampened by the steam. Her apron was sodden from the constant stance at the sink. All she could mutter was, 'So he's dun it agin, the stupid man.' She sauntered back to the farmhouse, head bent in hot pursuit to "give 'im a right piece of her mind", and she gave me strict instructions to "stay in barn till it was all over".

At dinner that night was an unnerving silence, apart from Pratt's foul habit of clicking his false teeth and pushing the lower set out with his tongue to annoy me. I felt sure that he was without doubt mentally unbalanced. Mabel leaned over and turned the oil lamp up. It sent a glow over the table.

'What yer do that fer, woman?'

'So as I can see yer antics, and when yer's put yer teeth back proper and yer mouth straight,' Mabel went on bravely, 'yer can apologise to Eve for yer tantrum at lunchtime. Well, come on, let's have it,' she said, 'yer was like a bellowing bull.'

At this moment I wanted so much to flee to my room, my stomach was churning; I did not think my legs would support me though, I was so afraid he would blow a gasket again but to my surprise he shifted nervously in his chair, then grunted with head bowed over his plate.

'Sorry gal.'

Mabel gulped, 'Think so too,' then lowered the lamp. In the lamp light his face was a ghastly pallor.

I turned to Mabel, Please will you excuse me, I have letters to write.' Pausing on my way out I rested my hand gently on Mabel's thin shoulder and whispered, 'Thank you.'

A smile crept over her tired worn face, 'Bring yer cocoa up later gal,' she said.

*

I packed my case ready for my getaway, then washed down in the bowl on the marble stand. Mabel had filled the jug with warm water for me. The candle light flickered around the room. It was sending shadows darting back and forth. Suddenly the door opened; my heart jumped nervously. It was only one of the cats, its shadow large like a tiger's. The day's fiasco had put me on edge.

I dressed quickly and was sitting up in bed when Mabel knocked on the door saying, 'It's only me dear,; My tiger was purring on the foot of the bed.

Mabel placed the mug of cocoa beside me and said, 'How long do you think you will stay here, dear?' She went on, 'The others did not stay long.'

'What others?' I replied, puzzled.

'Well, land girls like yerself.'

'But I thought I was the first.'

'Gawd no,' was her reply, 'there have been six, one only stayed a day; it be his drinking mek 'im techy, but it'll be alright tomorrow.'

I did not have the heart to tell her that my plans were to depart.

Dramatically, Mabel's shadow touched the ceiling, her sharp features were accentuated by the unflattering candle light; her nose seemed to get longer and be consumed by the door as she departed.

*

The telegram came just as we had finished milking the next morning. Pratt grunted when I read it out to him. The young lad was awaiting my reply, so I was spared any abuse. Also, at that precise time the travelling salesman drove up into the yard with his van bursting with cans of paraffin, candles, wicks for the oil lamps, glass mantles, saucepans hanging on string, scrubbing brushes, broom handles, everything but the kitchen sink. Rushing into the house I gave Mabel the telegram to read. She was so kind I felt the urge to hug her to me and tell her the truth, but then it would be her life I would be intruding into too, and after all I was just a passing stranger.

I hugged Mabel. 'I'm so sorry I have to go Mabel.'

'Quick Eve, go and ask Harry the salesman to give you a lift to the station,' she said.

'Certainly my love, hop in,' was his reply when I asked.

'I will just get changed into my uniform, will not be long, and many thanks Harry.'

'I'll get you there in time, just got one more farm to drop off some candles and pans,' he called out.

Poor Mabel looked so sad and crestfallen. Standing there waving to me, she called out: 'Come back and see me one day Eve, I will miss you.'

I felt a pang of guilt, but no way could I stay there to work with Pratt – he was a nightmare.

*

The station was deserted, Harry carried my suitcase onto the platform and went in search of the stationmaster. He strutted out of the office with Harry in his wake. Looking very important and pleased with himself, his thumbs tucked into his waistcoat, he strutted along the platform, smiling at me. Harry was in deep conversation with him, so I presumed he was telling him my tale of woe. I was beginning to feel like a VIP, perhaps he will attach a label to me. Apparently I was to travel in the goods wagon with Albert.

' 'Ere it be,' announced the station master with flag and whistle in his hand, 'it be on its way.'

There was a huddled conversation about me as the stationmaster vanished into the goods wagon, then a jolly smiling face looked over the stationmaster's stocky shoulders. He rushed past him, picked up my suitcase and beckoned me to follow. He covered a tea chest with mail bags for me to sit on. The other passengers were three crates of pigeons, and a silent member – a coffin. The pigeons were off to help with the war effort by carrying messages.

Albert was a cheerful man and his sense of humour was hilarious. He shared his packed lunch with me, which was bacon sandwiches, and his flask of tea which he said "had body in it". It was laced with Whisky. We toasted our silent member and when the train went over bumps it shot from one end of the wagon to the other.

'Hope he don't shout out,' said Albert, 'cause I ain't got any more tea with the body in it left,' and he fell about laughing. 'Look, we got bars on windows, so he can't get out.'

On reaching my destination I was feeling on cloud nine. Albert was holding onto the wagon door, swaying around, waving a red flag and shouting out, 'Up the Land Girls.' He sang *For she's a jolly good fellow,* followed at the top of his voice by, *Goodbye, goodbye, my lovely brown-eyed maiden,* and *I will see you in my dreams.*

I felt a lovely warm glow. Albert had lifted my spirits, and I think the whisky helped too! I waved him goodbye as I descended the stairway to the entrance below. I could still hear him singing when I walked out of the station.

* * *

CHAPTER TWENTY
AIR RAID

I had made my way to Head Office to request a posting to another farm, it was later in the afternoon when I reached my destination. After I left the office I was caught up in an air raid, the siren wailed out and I hurried towards the air raid shelters. The traffic had come to a standstill, there was a screeching of brakes, people were running in all directions, I was pushed along by the crowd. Then, like a fusillade of bullets we were scuttling for the open doors of the shelter. There was the distant pop-pop-popping of the anti-aircraft guns.

'Get in there quick lass,' said a voice behind me, my feet did not touch the steps. Going down to the shelter I was just carried along by the rush of bodies. I was helpless. I think this was more frightening than taking my chances outside.

Suddenly I was lifted aloft by a very tall Yank, who said in a Texan drawl, 'Lonesome Pine at your service honey, where would ya like your fanny parked.'

I was lost for words. He dropped me on a bunk alongside an elderly lady who was twisting her rosary beads in her hands, muttering nervously in prayer, 'Hail Mary, full of grace, the Lord is with thee, blessed art thou . . .'

For a split second there was silence, then the earth above us shuddered, Lonesome Pine comforted the old lady whose sobbing broke the silence.

Then came a second tremor which covered us all in dust. Lonesome Pine caught most of it, his head skimmed the ceiling. He tucked the old lady under his arm and with his other arm he clasped me to him with such force that I was finding it difficult to breathe and felt sure the button of his tunic would be imprinted on my forehead forever. I tried to call out but no sound came forth. Then, bless her, the old lady let out a wail and he released me from his iron grasp. I choked in the thick grey dust and he fell like a stone to the ground. He had been hit on the back of the head by a beam. The last I saw of Lonesome was him being carried out on a stretcher by the Red Cross helpers.

'That was a close shave,' remarked the old lady, crossing her chest.

'What a brave man was that gentle giant,' I said to the air raid warden.

'Don't worry about him lass, only knocked out, he'll be alright,' he assured me. 'Now up you go, that last one must have been pretty near, so mind how you go dear.'

*

I followed the crowd out into the bright sunlight. Wearily I made my way home. The roof of a warehouse had been blown off, the blackened face of the clock on the wall was still intact with the hands pointing to 2.15. Civil Defence workers were trying to move the dead and injured. I walked on through more carnage, seeing fractured water pipes gushing gallons of water down the street. There was a strange silence, occasionally shattered by a crack, and then a thud of falling masonry. There was no hysteria or panic, only the quiet desperation of the first aid teams and the shocked dazed stares of the onlookers. I felt a deep sadness for all. I walked on through the debris, the water splashing my legs.

There was a bath swinging from a telegraph pole, all twisted where the blast had thrown it. Houses were sliced in half, in one of the bedrooms an elderly lady was still lying in bed with a picture behind her bed hanging at an angle with the words, "Bless this House" on it. The wallpaper, with a rose design, was torn at the edges where the blast had ripped the house apart. Under the bed was still the chamber pot and the old lady's fur-edged slippers. There was twisted metal everywhere.

A passing helper remarked to me, 'This is a time when you wish you had a camera with you because a sight like that is unbelievable. My God, that dear old soul had a lucky day.'

We stood and looked up as our eyes met the old lady's, she smiled a wan smile and waved her hand to me. *What a shock,* I thought, *to have your whole house cut in half and still be alive!*

'Help is on the way Gran, lie still,' the helper said. She nodded her head to him. I learned later that the old lady had been bedridden for some time.

That awful day had taken the lives of many, also from the munitions factory by the railway line, where a bomb had been dropped on the place where many of the workers were on their way out for a lunch break. There were broken bodies scattered all over the railway line.

I walked on, picking my way over the debris, not knowing what would be around the corner. The eerie silence was all around me, fractured gas pipes stuck grotesquely out of the road, and there was a horrible smell of rotten eggs. I hurried on, trying to hold my breath. On walking into the next street all the houses were standing apart from the windows which had been blown out by the blast; but there was not a soul in sight. I felt completely alone, I turned the corner – it was still deserted.

Then I came on to the main road. Thank God I could hear the sound of traffic and people, and children playing hopscotch on the pavement outside their houses. A little lad rushed past me chasing a hoop and I sighed with relief that I had left the nightmare behind me. It was like stepping out of time warp. To think that only a short distance away was all that devastation.

*

I got my transfer from Pratt's farm the following week. It was about 5 miles from my friends so I met up with them quite often. It was a dairy farm and the farmer's name was Bernie Cole – his nickname was Puffer. He was rather on the large side, with a round jolly face and eyes that twinkled.

He was a very patient man and his way of giving orders went like this, 'Well now Eve, would you do me the favour of milking the cows today. Just take your time, don't rush, then push off back to hostel at four thirty, don't want yer slogging away 'ere at all hours, young lass like you should have time to enjoy life.' I was beginning to wish I could stay here longer but it was only for two months. He was a gentleman.

The other girls at the hostel remarked, 'What have you got that we haven't?' I was not sure, but it certainly was a refreshing change from what I had had to endure from Pratt.

He always made sure that the work on the farm was done in a very easy manner. Some days I rode with him to herd the cattle into the yard for milking.

'Why tramp all the way across those fields when we have hosses to ride on?' he would say.

His wife, Jeannie, was a gentle lady and so kind, lunch was always laid up for all the workers in the kitchen. They had two sons, Ricky and Billy. Ricky helped his dad on the farm, he was my age, 18. Billy was eighteen months older and awaiting his call up into the Royal Air Force. Ricky suffered from asthma so was exempt.

Billy invited me to go along with him to the Young Farmers' Dance. He assured me that he would provide transport. 'Be ready for 7.30 sharp,' were his parting words, 'evening dress, mind.'

So it was with great surprise when he appeared on a motorbike outside the hostel. He noted my look of horror. 'W-Well, well,' he stammered, 'the old man would not lend me the car.'

'Well, the only thing to do then Billy, is for me to tuck my long dress up my knicker legs!' He stared with mouth open. 'Here Billy, put my shoes in your pockets and let's go.' I said. We roared through the village with the locals casting looks of disapproval. At least we made quite a stir outside the dance hall.

Needless to say I had quite a number of admirers during the course of the evening but explained that it was not my usual way of travel but was a case of compromise in a desperate situation. It was either that or walk in my high heels, in which case I wouldn't have got far. They were quite disappointed. Bill and I laughed about it for a long time.

'Shall we repeat it?' he joked.

'Not likely,' I replied, 'we will hire a taxi next time and go in style.'

'Oh, what a shame,' he said, 'that was fun.'

'I'm sure your dad would not think so,' I retorted, 'more than likely he'd get the idea I was leading you astray.'

*

The next day, Billy and I had been asked by his dad to take the crates of cabbages to market. We set out around 7.30, but on the way Billy had to change the wheel on the van because of a puncture. So it made us late; we arrived there about 8.30. The market was filling up with serious shoppers, housewives anxious to buy fresh cream and fruit and vegetables. They heaped their bags and baskets and scurried back to the village bus which was awaiting them on the market edge. We quickly made our way to the stalls that were taking the cabbages and then did a quick tour around the market.

I loved to observe the people, it fascinated me. The way they sauntered over to the stalls they would pick over the second hand clothes, wander among the aisles of stalls picking things up and putting them down, with no intention of buying, and they came to meet their friends, exchange news and gossip. There was a stall selling tea and coffee and a man with a long greasy beard selling roast chestnuts. Billy handed me a bag of coconut ice.

'Come on Eve, we can't hang around here, Dad will think we have absconded,' he said. I was reluctant to leave. Markets had always held a certain fascination for me, there was so much life there and so many characters to observe.

*

With milking over for the day, I left the farm that evening to meet up with Rose, Josie and Dusty; we had all been invited to Meg's party, she was 21. To celebrate we were going to cycle to the Hob Nails Pub.

The evening went well, we played skittles with the Yanks but they won as usual. On the way home Madge cycled into the ditch and we spent an age looking around for her lamp which had fallen into all the mud and gunge.

We had to take it in turns to hold her on the cycle, she said, I felt alright in the pub, it was when I got into the fresh air . . .'

We were halfway back to the hostel when some black Yanks came from nowhere, there must have been about 20 of them at a guess. They called out, 'Stop honeys!' Some were standing in a line across the road directly ahead of us, the rest chasing behind on cycles.

'Oh hell,' I screamed out, 'pedal as fast as you can, head into them, hang in there Madge, here we go.' With heads down I sped towards the line. Thank God it worked; they jumped out of the way, one grabbed Rose's foot, but she kicked out and struck him in his neck.

'Honey, stop!' he shouted.

'Sod off,' was Rose's rude reply.

I glanced back and could see Josie and Dusty pedalling like mad, then to my horror this big black Yank cycled alongside me in the dark, it was difficult to see him. He stretched out his hand to grab my handlebars, but luckily he lost his balance and fell onto the road. Rose and I were still holding on to Madge's saddle. Thank God she had had the sense to keep pedalling. My arms and shoulders ached from holding her on, it was a relief when we had put quite a distance between them and us.

Josie called out, 'Let's stop for a rest, my legs ache.'

'Keep going,' I shouted back, 'they may still try to catch up with us.' We were thankful to see the hostel and to feel safe. We all were accounted for, and never again did we cycle out there at night. A few days later, after that episode, we heard about two girls being attacked and the suspects were three black Yanks. We all agreed that luck was with us that night and we thanked God for having the presence of mind not to panic. Thank God they were not good cyclists.

*

My time on the Coles' Farm was coming to an end. Billy was now in the Air Force and stationed in Scotland. We promised to write. We were all sad when he left – to me he was a good friend. Some day he would marry some lucky girl – *Will make a good husband,* I thought.

Mr Coles (Puffer) said I was always welcome to return, but that was not up to me, I had to go where I was sent. *Now* I wondered, *what will the next place be like?*

* * *

CHAPTER TWENTY-ONE
HATCHETT'S FARM

I was sent to a farm out in the sticks to do dairy work and help around the farm generally. A Mr Hatchett, the farmer, would meet me at the station. I was informed I was to look out for a tall good-looking dark-haired gentleman. I mused, thinking this would be an ideal situation for Josie.

On coming out of the station I did not see anyone answering that description, the only other person standing in this God-forsaken place was a scruffy tramp wearing a battered felt hat which would have done justice to a scarecrow, a dirty old Mac hanging in rags, fringing around muck-splattered gumboots.

I walked up and down thinking perhaps I had alighted at the wrong station and was just about to turn on my heel and walk back into the station when the tramp headed in my direction.

I delved into my pockets for a few coins thinking he was after the price of a cup of tea, and was just about to hand him the coins when he lifted his battered felt hat and said, 'Mornin', be you the new Land Girl for Hatchett's Farm?'

I stammered, 'Y-Yes.'

'Follow me then gal, my car's this way. Ere be me old jalopy then.' He pointed to an old Austin Seven that had seen better days.

'I only hope it is safe, I thought nervously, and was convinced by now that the tramp was one of the farm labourers sent to collect me. He put his hand on the car door – I could not believe my eyes, the door of the car fell forward, dangling on one hinge.

'Hang on a mo, gal,' he calmly said, 'whilst I git some string.' He dug down into his tatty Mac pocket and produced a length of string, threaded it painstakingly through two holes in the rusted bodywork, muttering, 'That'll do it.'

I looked on in amazement, *Hope he takes the corners steady,* I thought, *a parachute would not go amiss in this contraption.*

'Well, come on then gal, let's 'ave yer case and we will be on our way,' he said. I was just about to get into the wreck when there was a squawk and a flurry of feathers passed my head.

'Oh bleeding 'ell, there goes Bessie,' he said, 'wait yer whilst I catch the little perisher.' He chased off along the station in hot pursuit to corner the chicken. It was leading him a merry dance, in no way did Bessie wish to be caught. She was enjoying her freedom too much.

I sat for a while watching this pantomime thinking *What the hell is going on? If he looks like that,* I mused, *what was the farmer like?* I dreaded to think what I would find at the end of my journey. *I suppose I could flee now,* I thought, *and catch the next train back home, but on second thoughts, if it is unbearable when I get there I will just have to call on dear departed Gran again to have yet another funeral.*

I surveyed the interior of the scrap heap – there was chicken shit all splattered up the dashboard, the roof lining of it was hanging down in places. I moved forward in my seat and to my horror realised it was not bolted to the floor.

So my imagination ran riot – I could see myself being flung into the elements of the countryside and what if he had to pull up sharp? I thought I would take my chances in the back. So I scrambled over the seats only to find, horror of horrors, Bessie's domain by all the signs. It looked like he had half the farmyard, on the seat there was straw, hay, more chicken muck, part of a lawn mower, children's toys. I pushed it along to the end of the seat, cleared myself a space and awaited his return.

When he eventually arrived he was puffing and blowing breathlessly from his chase, and tucked tightly under his arm was Bessie.

'Oh, so there you are gal, in back. Why there?'

I replied, 'Because the seat in the front is mobile. I thought it would be safer to sit in the back.'

He chuckled, 'Ah, yer don't trust me then.'

'W-Well, I didn't mean that,' I stammered.

'Well, you'll 'ave to tek Bessie then and keep an eye on 'er. Can't be doing with her flying about now can I?' he said. I grasped the chicken and placed her on top of the collection of straw and hay, her neck kept going back and forth in my direction and I was on edge in case she pecked me.

'My name's Stephen,' he offered, 'Steve to my friends. And yours? he asked.

'Evelyn,' I replied, 'Eve to my friends too.'

'Well Evie, I hope you are going to like the farm. My wife and the two little ones are looking forward to meeting you.'

Oh God, I thought, *I am going to be billeted with him.*

*

After three attempts to get the car started he was beginning to get flustered and he threatened to get an axe and chop it in half and throw it on the scrap heap – the engine then turned over and we chugged along on our way. He chatted to me and told me about his children, Jessica who was 18 months old and Steve junior, 4 years old. I asked him what the farmer was like and he replied with a hearty chuckle.

'I think he is a smashing chap, kind and considerate and very handsome,' he added. It was seven miles to the farm and along these country roads there were plenty of pot holes so he would kindly shout out, 'Hang in there, put yer hand on Bessie, 'ere comes another.'

I should think Bessie travelled this way quite often for she nestled down in the hay and did not flutter a feather, thank goodness. I had visions again of being pecked. It certainly was a bone-shaker and I was expecting the string to snap and the door to fly away, but more by luck than by judgment it stayed put.

*

On arriving at the farm, the children were jumping up and down by the gate, then ran towards the car to greet us. Bessie fluttered out squawking to the farmyard. We were greeted by his wife Madge, who ushered me into the farmhouse.

Steve Hatchet confessed to me that he was in fact the farmer and he had dressed up like a tramp for a bet with his brother.

'What about the car?' I said.

'Oh that,' he replied, 'well, we have had it on the farm for years and Bob and I fixed the engine last week so I thought it a good idea to use it to pick you up from the station. Well, you must admit it was funny, wasn't it? Your face when the door fell off and Bessie flew out – I wish I had had my camera,' he said.

'You nearly lost a Land Girl,' I replied, 'for when you were chasing Bessie, I was in two minds to catch the next train back home. I thought I was coming to a funny farm,' I added.

His wife said, 'He is always larking about, you will get used to it.' Personally, I was not so sure about that. I might have to call upon dear old Gran again, for I had never been overly keen on practical jokers.

*

My work on the farm was to feed the animals and take care of the orphan lambs (which were a joy to feed), with the help of the children. Then I was asked to take the pony and trap to the school to pick up the little boy. This was to become a regular occurrence and I went along with it for a time. Hatchett's wife, Madge, would argue with her husband where I would be that day, but after all, I was a Land Girl not a home help, and I told them that. So I decided to solve the problem myself as they did not seem able to. I found alternative accommodation in the village with a retired farmer named George, and his wife Gladys.

Hatchett was furious and demanded I went back to live in the farmhouse. He ranted on, 'What's my wife going to do without your help?'

I replied with anger, 'The same as before I came here. You will have to get a home help, for my place is on the farm.'

I found being billeted away from the farm was a bonus as I was able to enjoy a more social life, and Rose often came to stay. She had a new boyfriend, Stanley, and seemed to be much happier these days after the split from Wiggins. I still thought a lot about Tom and was rather wary about getting involved at this present time with anyone else.

* * *

CHAPTER TWENTY-TWO
V.E. DAY

The whole Hatchett family and myself were haymaking when news came through that war had ended with Germany. I stayed most of the day pitching the hay into piles and was not sure what I was to do – carry on or celebrate.

Bob Hatchett solved my dilemma; he sprinted across the field towards me, retrieved the pitchfork from my hand and said, You are going home to celebrate right now. I have the car in the lane.'

His brother, Steve, protested, 'What about the hay?'

'Bugger the hay, you inconsiderate pig, this young girl is off home now to celebrate with the rest of her colleagues.'

On the way he remarked, 'That brother of mine is beyond me, no consideration at all. He should have downed tools when the news first came over the radio and taken you home. I suppose you realise he is stony broke, lazy sod, keeps asking for handouts from our dad, spends half his time in bed in the mornings.'

'I know all about it,' I replied, 'well, get away from here, that is my advice to you, it's only going to get worse.'

On arriving in the town, it was so packed with crowds of people, soldiers, airmen, American, Polish, they were all whooping it up – it was a sight to behold. Traffic had come to a complete standstill. Everyone, young or old, was dancing and waving a Union Jack. Some had climbed lampposts and were tying flags and balloons around the tops.

Bob said, 'Go on Eve, join the throng and enjoy yourself. Forget the farm, come back next week and hand in your notice to that brother of mine. Go on now, live it up,' he let out a deep sigh, 'wish I was coming with you.'

*

On stepping out of the car I thanked him and before I knew what was happening I was whisked away by a handsome Yank.

'Come on Honey, let's dance.' We danced around the lampposts, the parked vehicles that had just been abandoned by their owners, and up and down the steps of the local council offices. Various bottles of drink were passed around – which was a mystery – perhaps the pubs along the streets were issuing it out.

Shaun (my dancing partner) said, 'Sugar, who cares? The war is over, we are happy, let's drink and be merry!'

Oh, how I wished it was Tom I was celebrating with . . .

'Oh Brown Eyes! Come on, don't look so sad, let's dance the rumba,' said my Yank partner.

I tried to escape after a while, it was getting too much, I wanted to get home and change into a cotton dress, something cool, I was so hot and sticky in my uniform. It was a perfect day with the sunshine and all I wanted was to be with my family, and then to join the celebrations which would most likely go on through the night.

'Just hang in there now Shaun,' I said, 'I must leave you and head for home.'

'Oh good,' he replied, 'I'll come too.'

'No, I don't think so,' I retorted.

'Then meet me later, Brown Eyes,' he called after me as I made my way through the crowd.

'Maybe,' I called back, 'maybe!'

It took me a good hour to battle my way through the crowds. On my way I was hugged by a sailor, kissed by an elderly gentleman who said "God bless you dear", I danced with a group of young Air Force cadets and ended up in the middle of the longest conga I have ever seen, but eventually broke away and ran home.

*

After changing into my cool cotton dress and sandals I sat for a while in the garden. My aunt was resting in the cool of her bedroom, and the rest of the family were out visiting. I felt I needed to sit alone for a while and think. It was warm and comfortable with the sun shining onto my face, my eyelids began to feel heavy, and then slowly closed.

The sun was warm on my bare arms, and listening to the almost silence I sat there wallowing in the luxury of the sensation, my mind raced to Tom and what might have been. Refusing to believe the finality of it all, and of all those thousands of people who, like me, had lost a loved one. Oh, the senselessness of it all, the sheer waste of young lives. Why . . . oh why? *What was it all for?* I asked myself time and time again.

* * *

CHAPTER TWENTY-THREE
THE DALTONS

My next farm was in Bewdley – the farmer, Mr Dalton, was the Mayor of the town. There was Elizabeth his wife, Pamela their eldest daughter (around my age), Margaret (17) who attended the local college, and Mary, 7 years of age. To complete this family unit were two servants, Alice the cook and Sarah the house maid.

They took it upon themselves to spoil me at dinner. Mr Dalton would carve the best slice of meat for me and add extra to my plate, saying, 'You need it for all the hard work you put in daily for us all on the farm.'

The cook, Alice, chipped in, 'You need building up – yer be like a yard of pump water.'

Sarah added, 'Just like two boards clapped together.'

I tried my utmost to explain that I had always been slender and that probably I had not as yet had time to grow into my body. They arranged for me to stay in the town with their retired Nanny Jessie, but to have all meals at the farm, until the time their building extension on the house was completed, which would be in three months time. Jessie just provided a room for me.

She was a lovely lady and was in the same mind as the family about my body – that I needed building up. So at night she would produce a large basin full of steaming bread with milk – the very smell turned my stomach. I always remarked to Jessie that it would be a good idea if I retired to my bed and ate it whilst reading my book but my protest fell on stony ground as she insisted that I ate it up. I think she thought I was one of her small charges going back to the days in the nursery when Nanny had to be obeyed.

Crikey, I thought, *I could end up like the side of a house with all this food pushed at me, what the heck am I going to do with it? I have got to get rid of it somewhere.* The house was late Victorian so no inside loo. *Ah,* I thought, *the windows!*

So I opened the bedroom window, drained the milk onto the hollyhocks that were growing alongside of the house, then threw the soggy bread onto the garden. The local cats got wind of this unexpected feast and gathered there every night for their supper.

Dear Jessie remained oblivious to where her bread and milk went, but remarked how well I looked and said, 'Yer getting more meat on yer bones Eve.'

After I moved into the farmhouse, Jessie came to visit and said that the neighbourhood cats crying out half the night were pestering her.

I wonder why, I thought, *could it be something to do with the bread and milk?*

*

On the farm working alongside me was Harold, who was a conscientious objector. He had refused point blank to be drafted into the army. 'So,' he said, 'the farm was the best of three evils, it was either a munitions factory, down the mines, or work on the land. He chose the latter.

He was stocky in build with very blue protruding eyes. To me they looked like glass marbles, it gave him a "startled" expression. He was allocated to do the heavy work, when I could find him – he had this clever knack of disappearing when anything heavy needed moving or lifting.

I would eventually find him hiding in the hayloft smoking his woodbines. He would grin at me, displaying a row of stained yellow and black teeth, like a naughty schoolboy found out for some misdemeanour.

Then there was Charlie the gardener. He lived next to the farmyard in a small cottage with his wife, May. He was quite old, about 75 at a guess, practically bent double with a hump on his back. Apparently he had been gored by a bull when he was a young man and was very lucky, by all accounts, to be alive today to tell the tale.

He had a permanent dewdrop which would hang from his nose getting longer every time his head lowered, it would travel way past his knees then he would take an almighty sniff and it would travel halfway back towards his nose then drip. From his trouser pocket he would produce a large handkerchief that looked more like the tail of his shirt and swiftly draw it in one quick swipe across his nose, half of the dewdrop would end up past his ear, poor man. Alice the cook said she would hand him his tea sideways in case it plopped into his mug! They all had great respect for old Charlie though, he was quite a character.

Mr Dalton had a large practice in the town so we did not see much of him around the farm. He had great faith in me though and would say before he left for the office, 'Well Eve, I leave the entirety in your capable hands.' At first I was in awe of being in charge, but with the help of Harold (when he was not in hiding) and old Charlie, the farm ran smoothly.

On the farm were two dairy cows, Freckles and Daisy, who I milked twice a day. There were four horses, about 50 grazing sheep in the far field and two pet lambs who had to be fed with the bottle. I named one "Bubbles" because it always blew bubbles of milk from the bottle when I fed it, and the other one Mary had named "Spot".

Then there were about 100 chickens, 20 geese and about 30 turkeys. Charlie took charge of the chickens and other fowl so my main job was to keep the dairy side of the farm ticking over. After milking I would put the milk through the cooling system in the dairy then separate the cream from the milk. Alice would take over from there and take what milk she needed for the house and take a quantity of the cream to make butter.

When Mary came home from school I would usually go with her down to the far field to catch two of the ponies, Copper and Briar, and we would ride out for a canter through the lanes around the farm.

Rose came quite often to visit, sometimes with Stanley, her new boyfriend. I did not see Josie and Dusty very often for they were still going out with their American boyfriends, who were expecting to go overseas to the Far East, so they wanted to spend all their spare time with them. I found it very lonely at times after living in the hostel. I thought about Tom a lot and missed him, so I filled my life as much as possible and concentrated on my jobs on the farm. In my spare time I knitted for the soldiers and charity. I enjoyed working for the Daltons, they were a lovely family.

While there I received a certificate from the Queen thanking me for my services to the country. It was a great honour. I never expected anything like that. I am sure Mr Dalton must have had something to do with it but when I enquired he just smiled and said, 'Congratulations, you deserve it Eve for all you have achieved and endured on the land, you never said, "I cannot do that" but just set to and tried. We have nothing but admiration for you.' I never expected any recognition, after all I was only doing a job to the best of my ability, but then on the other hand it was nice to be appreciated.

We had a problem with the cow Freckles. She was off her food and looking very sorry for herself. We contacted the vet and he came out and prescribed a drench. He was a short stocky little man, not very long in the arm, so needed a box to stand on to administer the evil smelling liquid.

'Will you be kind enough to stick your fingers up her nose, Eve, whilst I pour this down her throat.'

I was rather taken aback for I had not ever had the unpleasant task of pushing my fingers up a cow's nose before! I thought, *Well, here goes . . .* It was weird, like sticking one's fingers into a jelly.

I ended up with some of the drench down my neck, a slimy substance. The vet had some trickle over his head too, and he remarked, 'I hope it's a good hair restorer!' He assured me that she would soon begin to feel better and left me another bottle to give her later.

Oh heck, I thought, *who can I ask to help me? Ah . . . Harold!* I looked in his favourite hiding place but he was not there. I asked old Charlie if he had seen him.

He replied, 'Look in haystack.'

'Haystack?' I questioned.

'Oh, ar,' he retorted, 'often see 'im down there.'

I needed his help so made my way across the field in search of him. It was no use asking Alice or Sara for help, they were scared of cows, so it had to be Harold.

I continued my way towards the haystack. In the field was a flock of sheep which closed ranks and stared at me, watching from a distance, except one chubby bouncing lamb who made a bee-line for me. He came up close, I spoke to him and stroked his face. He may have been one of the lambs I had bottle fed but I was not sure. I walked on thinking he had rejoined the flock, then I felt this almighty thud in my legs and I went sprawling forward into the grass with the lamb standing over me, bleating! It *was* Bubbles looking at me as if to say, "Do you not recognise me?" Alice said he was probably peeved because I did not have a bottle for him. He followed behind me, bleating, the other sheep just looked on with that expression of "silly lamb"!

*

On arrival at the haystack there was no sign of Harold and I was just about to walk back across the field when I saw cigarette smoke rising from the far end of the stack. I called out *'Harold'*.

He poked his head out from his hideaway and shouted down, 'What's wrong?'

'Firstly Harold,' I said, 'what on earth are you doing? You could set fire to the whole haystack. I need your help in the cowshed to give the cow a drench.'

'Ask old Charlie,' he replied.

'Charlie is not up to it,' I retorted, 'it needs someone stronger. Please, Harold,' I pleaded.

'Oh alright then, I'll come presently,' he replied, 'just let me have forty winks. Don't worry gal, I'll be there,' he reassured me.

'Why are you tired?' I questioned.

'Had a late night,' was his reply, 'little drop too much to drink, but don't 'ee let on to the Guv'nor, will you gal?' he pleaded.

I walked back to the farmyard with Bubbles bleating behind me. I had a conversation with the lamb, 'Well Bubbles,' I said, 'what shall we do about Harold? He is becoming quite a problem.'

'Baa baa,' was his reply. He was quite disappointed when I shut the gate behind him as he was quite prepared to keep on following me.

I met old Charlie on the way, and he remarked, 'Did yer find him then?'

'Yes, he is on his way,' I said.

He retorted, 'Next week, or week after!'

Well, I thought, *we will have to do something about Harold. No doubt Josie and Rose would have some good ideas...!*

Charlie was going to the yard to get an air rifle to take some pot shots at the rooks, who he said were pests, they had been swooping down into the chicken pens and eating the food, and Alice was wanting more eggs for the house. I could hear old Charlie pop, pop, popping away with the rifle. I presumed Harold had long since vacated his hiding place, when suddenly, a piercing scream came from the haystack. There was Harold jumping up and down waving his arms in the air having hysterics. The rooks were circling around the haystack. He was shouting abuse at old Charlie but he still kept on firing.

'You silly old bugger,' said Harold as he practically fell off the stack, 'it's me Harold, not a bleeding rook.'

'Well, how was I to know that?' said wily Charlie, 'all I could see were these black feathers moving up and down, and besides if yer be on payroll same as us, then yer should not have been in haystack, let that be a lesson to yer. From now on, I am going to have the rifle handy to scare away the rooks!'

Problem solved for now, I thought – well done Charlie!

*

Harold had been given the job of re-wiring a fence, but instead of getting rid of the excess wire he had just loosely slipped it over the branch of an apple tree. One of the loops of wire was hanging precariously a short way from the ground, so when the store pigs escaped from their pens and rampaged through the orchard, one unlucky pig managed to put his head through the wire. The more he struggled the tighter the wire gripped his neck like a noose, so that when I arrived on the scene the pig was literally swinging through the air. There was no-one around to help; I tried putting my fingers through the wire but it was so tight that it was hopeless. The poor pig was frantic and squealing.

I ran towards the farmhouse to get help, but the only person there was Elizabeth Dalton; Alice and Sara were on their afternoon off. Harold was nowhere to be seen and old Charlie was out rabbiting. Elizabeth held the pig while I cut the wire with the cutters. It fell to the ground with a thud and we were sure it was dead, but it got up after a few minutes, shook itself then ran off with the others. We managed to herd them all together and get them all safely back into the pens. Needless to say the pig only lived two days, they found it dead in the pen one morning.

Harold was told to pull himself together or else his services would not be needed. He stayed on the farm for about three months then managed to get a contracting job working on different farms, a few days at a time.

Old Charlie said, 'That will suit him fine, day in bed, day at work.' We managed quite well without him.

Mr Dalton eventually employed a young lad who had just left school. He came in part time – his name was Bert and he was about 5' 6", stockily built with a round chubby face and eyes that twinkled when he smiled. He was funny and had a wicked sense of humour, but at least he was always around when needed. Old Charlie warmed to him and always sent him home with something for his supper, a rabbit or pigeon.

Bert was the oldest of seven children, his dad was in the army, an infantry soldier, so his mum had quite a struggle to make ends meet. They lived in the village in one of the estate cottages. Bert told us that they did not have any indoor water but had to draw it from the well each day, and the toilet was down the garden. Apparently they all slept in one bed, the children that is, "three at the top and three at the bottom", said Bert, and the baby slept with his Mam.

His brothers and sisters sent a message with their brother to ask me if I would visit because they wanted to see a Land Girl. They all lined up outside the cottage door to meet me, I think they were quite disappointed to see I was human.

Bert said, 'Gawd knows what they thought yer looked like, gal, perhaps they thought yer had two heads.'

The eldest girl, Maisie, I noticed was the only one wearing shoes. Alice informed me they could only afford shoes for Bert and Maisie, the others had to go barefoot. We all helped out, Alice and I knitted socks and gloves for them, and the Daltons sent Bert home every Friday with a box of vegetables, also we would take the tractor and trailer out to collect wood for their fire. Old Charlie's wife, May, baked homemade bread and scones and at Christmas time we made toys. May taught me how to make dolls and soft toys. We had quite a good production line going – teddy bears, rabbits, golliwogs etc. It was such a success that what was left over we gave to the Children's Home and the Church for their bazaar. Jessie was keen to help too. I learned from her how to embroider and make a tablecloth out of a flour sack, dressing gowns from old army grey blankets and dolls' houses from cardboard boxes.

*

Rose and Josie came for the weekend. We went to the cinema in Kidderminster to see "Top Hat" with Ginger Rogers and Fred Astaire.

Josie's boyfriend, Paul, was in the Far East on the front line, so it was a worrying time for her. Dusty's boyfriend, Ty, was sure that any day he would be sent out. The only reason he was still here was because he had an accident on his motorbike after an argument with a tree, "the tree won", said Rose.

*

There was talk that the war would be over soon. We had a letter from Head Office in Birmingham to say that it would take a year or more to wind down the Land Army and asked if we would carry on until then. Josie remarked that she would be off back to Brum and on no account was she hanging around. She had had enough of farm work.

'Do you remember Josie,' Rose remarked, 'that you were on the look out for a rich farmer, and a handsome one to boot?' Josie laughed.

'I have come down to earth since then, grown up I suppose.'

'What will you do Rose,' I said, 'when the war is over?'

'I may go back to being a nippy in the Lyons Corner Café,' said Rose, 'I rather enjoyed that, and we did get good tips. Or I may marry Stanley and live happily ever after! And you Eve?' said Rose, 'what about you?'

'Well,' I said, 'I don't want a 9 to 5 job, it will have to be something that presents a challenge. I will know when the opportunity presents itself,' I added, 'but I will carry on here until my services are not required.'

* * *

CHAPTER TWENTY-FOUR
BEN THE BULL

That next week I was sent to Yew Tree Farm, three miles from the Daltons, to spend two weeks, as the dairy man had been called up for the army and the farmer there was having difficulties finding someone to do the milking. Bert took over my job and I went to help out. They had a small herd of Friesian cows. It was not an exacting job but I had to rise earlier and be there for 6.30 in the morning to do the milking, then return at 9.30 to the Daltons to take over from Bert, then back to Yew Farm again for milking at 3.30.

Mr Harris was a jolly person, he was a rotund figure with a large stomach. He wore old-fashioned waistcoats with a gold watch chain dangling in the front.

He had a habit of twisting the watch around, opening the back and putting it to his ear, then he would say, "Well, well, time marches on. We will do this, then that." Then he would stand back on his heels and rock back and forth looking very pleased with himself as though he had accomplished quite a lot in that short time. I very much liked his "we will" because he did not stay around long enough to put it into practice but appeared back on the scene when the tasks had been accomplished. Then it would be "We did very well, Eve, didn't we?" Then his line would begin all over again, 'Well, let's see before you go back to the farm."

'We will,' I usually remarked, 'well, Mr Harris, time marches on, must go now, time does fly when you are busy!' He would look at me under his eyes not sure how to take me. With all his concentration on time I think that he thought of me as a permanent fixture there to work around his timepiece. Personally, I think he missed his true vocation and would have done well in politics or on the stage – an ideal Mr Pickwick.

*

There was another Land Girl on the farm, Sally, but I did not come into contact with her very often. She was always out in the fields with the tractor. I did get help with the milking, in the form of Stewart, Mr Harris's son, who had just left school. He was a replica of his dad except for the stomach and watch.

I was just about to cycle back to the Dalton's farm when "Mr Pickwick" came striding over, looking very smart in his hunting outfit, twisting his watch chain, the usual procedure, tapping the case of his watch and placing it near his ear.

Stewart quipped, 'What's the time, Dad? Is it time for tea?'

He looked over at his son, screwed up his eyes and said, 'Cheeky young tike. Before you go on your way Eve dear, I have a proposition to put to you,' he said, 'we are thinking about putting Ben the Bull in the local show and we wondered if you and Sally would like to get him ready for the grand occasion?'

I was, to say the least, taken aback by this request. When I did regain my composure I replied, 'Well, I must say, no thankyou, Mr Pick... er Harris, it sounds too dangerous a task to undertake.'

He laughed, rocking back and forth on his heels, twisting his timepiece round and round. 'He be as gentle as a lamb, my dear, right docile,' he chuckled.

Where have I heard that before? I thought.

He laughed again, 'Just like a little puppy dog,' he remarked.

I mentioned to Alice about Mr Harris' unusual request, 'Oh, it be true Eve, he is gentle, I have seen her walking him down the lanes,' she said, 'but be on the safe side,' she warned, 'make sure you are not alone with him, just in case like. Better to be safe than sorry dear.' She added, 'we want you back here in one piece don't we?'

I still had my doubts about this bull. *I will have to go and pay him a visit and see for myself,* I thought.

Stewart had a small brown mongrel dog which he called Penny. Penny would weave her way through the stalls in the cowshed, she would nose her way into the byres diving out with a mouth full of the cows' food, chewing away on the cow cake and chasing the farm cats that wandered in at milking time. She was as bright as a button. She followed me down to the bullpen. I looked over at Ben snoring away on the straw. Before I could stop her, Penny leapt over into the pen and began to lick the bull's face, he just opened one eye and looked at her, snorted then rolled back to sleep. I was amazed. Must be true after all then. Calling Penny back over, I went up to the farmyard to look for Sally.

Sally was a very well built girl with a shock of ginger hair, a pleasant face with large round eyes that crinkled at the corners when she smiled.

'Is it about young Ben and the grooming we have to undertake?' she said, 'I caught sight of you peeking in at him. What do you think then Evie?'

'Well,' I replied, 'from what I see, he is exactly as they say, docile. When do you want me to help you?' I enquired.

'Would tomorrow morning be OK?' she asked, 'at about 9.30, after milking?'

'See you then.'

*

I met Sally that morning at Ben's pen, she was armed with a bucket, cloths and brushes.

'Before I go in Sally, is he tied up?' I asked nervously.

'Of course, it would be impossible to groom him otherwise,' she retorted. Deep down I was still not convinced, but I did not like the look in his eye, it was a look like "I am going to get you". Everything went well, I brushed and combed his tail and his back, he looked as though he was enjoying all this attention and closed his eyes.

'I am just going to pop out to get some more water,' Sally called out to me, 'I'll be about two ticks.'

'Don't go please,' I pleaded, 'what happens if he moves over too far to the side?'

'Oh, I don't think he will do that, but if he does, just give his tail a hard twist, then he will move over,' she shouted back.

'Come back quick, Sally,' I called after her.

She laughed back, 'He won't hurt you!'

I carried on brushing him. I noticed he was getting restless, perhaps if I talked to him it would calm him down. Nervously I told him he was a fine bull. He grew more and more agitated, tossed his head, pawed the ground then moved over with such force he pushed his side into me, and kept on pushing until I was smack bang against the wooden partition. He kept pushing. I could hear the creaking of the wood behind me – my body was gradually being crushed. To say I was scared was an understatement.

I called out to Sally, 'Help, help, anybody out there, help.' I knew I had to do something quickly so I stretched over his rump, grabbed his tail and gave it an almighty twist! He moved with such force I thought he would pull the rings out of the wall. I was out of that pen like a rocket, did not stop to open the half door, just vaulted over. I kept on running to put as much distance as possible between him and me.

'Hey, hey,' shouted Mr Pickwick, 'what's going on, hold on gal. My God, Eve, you are as white as a sheet,' he said, 'come, sit down, tell me what is it?'

I stammered, 'I-It's, i-it's your <u>docile</u> bull, nearly crushed me against the wall in the pen,' I breathlessly told him.

'Well, well, that is a great surprise to me, him being always gentle and all – a great surprise. Well, I'll be damned,' he retorted, twisting his watch chain. 'I wonder what upset him today, perhaps he had the belly ache, what do you think?' he said.

'I didn't stay there long enough to find out!' I replied, 'but I bet his tail end is sore.'

'We will have to cancel him for the show, can't take a chance now.' He sat there looking at the earth with his head in his hands, 'Ah well, life is full of surprises,' he said, 'I'll be damned if it ain't.'

Mr Pickwick was more concerned about that evil bull than me. I walked away angry and in disgust. Mr Dalton was furious when I told him of the day's events. Needless to say I did not return to the Harris' farm. They did ask for my help when Stewart was off sick but the Daltons said no.

* * *

CHAPTER TWENTY-FIVE
V.J. DAY

It was one of those sizzling hot days when the only place you want to be is in the swimming pool, I was just walking down to the field to bring the cows up for milking when a very excited Bert came running down towards me shouting, War is over, war is over! Mr Dalton is awaiting you at the house, Eve,' he breathlessly informed me, 'you are getting a lift home to join the celebrations.'

'But I just can't go like that,' I protested, 'I have the milking to do.'

'You can Eve,' retorted Bert proudly, 'I am taking over for you.'

Mr Dalton was there waiting for me, 'Go on in dear,' he said, 'pack a bag for an overnight stay and we will see you back here tomorrow night.'

*

It was chaotic when I arrived home, there were street parties in full swing, it was VE Day all over again. All nationalities were dancing and drinking. I was swept along with the crowds, two elderly ladies linked my arms and practically carried me along to join their street party. I sat with their families, friends and neighbours, ate jelly and blancmange with the children, danced with two sailors, then about two hours later managed to get home, feeling very woozy but happy.

There was party in full swing there, so more celebrating. I was so tipsy it was with great difficulty that I at last managed to get into bed, for it seemed to have a mind of its own and was moving around the room. I rang Rose the next day, so we could all meet up for a celebration of our own. We arranged to meet up in Birmingham.

It seemed very strange and quiet to walk the streets of Birmingham after all the trauma of the air raids. At least now we could go places and not be afraid that it may be our last, and we could relax in the cinema and watch to the end of a film without rushing out to the nearest air raid shelter when the sirens sounded.

'That reminds me,' I said to Rose, 'we have yet to see the other half of *"Gone with the Wind!"*'

It was so nice to be all together again. We spent a lovely time, talked over old times, Josie kept us laughing about Big Lil and Merv's antics. Josie's boyfriend Paul was still overseas and she was hoping that now the war was over that he would be able to come to England before being discharged. She was worried that he might go directly home to the States. Dusty and Ty were engaged and had planned to get married in about two months time. Rose was still going steady with Stanley.

It was lovely that the war was over but we would all soon travel our separate ways in life. We all promised to keep in touch, which we did for a while. But for now it was the end of an amazing chapter in our lives, it was goodbye to all those characters we met both on the farms and socially. Would we, I wondered, be able to settle into civilian life after all the adventures on the farms?

Rose's reply when I put it to her was, 'Bloody 'ell Eve, I can't wait, the only ones I will miss are you and the rest of the gang! You and your deep thinking is beyond me. Now, there's an idea for you, or should I say challenge? Write a book; here's a good title,' she offered, *"The Forgotten Army".'* Overworked, underpaid, and don't forget to put in the hazards of working on the land; how we had to run the gauntlet not only from the animals but some of the over-amorous males we had to work alongside. Oh, and not to forget the randy "Ities".'

Rose had a very frightening encounter with an Italian prisoner of war, Lorenzo, when we were threshing. Apparently he jumped out on Rose when everyone had gone to the barn to eat their lunch. She had stayed behind to look for her lunch box which was missing from the back of her cycle. But by all accounts he came off decidedly worse for wear – Rose gave him a sharp kick which she said would change his voice to soprano. He certainly made a grave mistake picking on Rose. He limped around the farm looking very sorry for himself afterwards.

*

I returned to the Daltons and stayed there for three months, and while there I had a very bad bout of flu which left me very weak an listless. So I was sent to the Women's Land Army Convalescent Home, Rest Break House in Torquay where Land Girls who needed rest to recuperate after illness or operations usually stayed – about a month until they were fit enough to return to the farms.

Mrs Dorothy Lake ran the home with a small staff. After a month there I was ready to return and tackle the work on the farm again but was given an offer I could not refuse by Mrs Lake, to stay and help her run the place, which I gladly accepted.

*

It was just what I needed, another challenge, another chapter to begin. I had the approval of my family. They were relieved that I was leaving the land. They thought that I had done more than my share of farm work and that this job would be easier for me, and at the end of the day more rewarding.

So I returned to the Daltons to give in my notice and also to the headquarters of the Women's Land Army, although I would still be attached to the service but in a different capacity.

It was sad saying goodbyes to the Daltons, they were a lovely family. Also Old Charlie, May and not forgetting Bert, and a fond farewell to the animals; I would miss them. I found that part of my job so rewarding and I shed a tear when I stroked the ponies, as well as Freckles and Daisy, not forgetting Jet the lovely black silky Labrador who I was always told not to pat because he was a gun dog, but when no-one was around I would give him a hug. It was sad to see him locked up in a pen alone, he was not allowed indoors, I was told "no petting on any account, he was a working dog".

*

Well, that was the end of my farm life – on to Torquay and Rest Break House to care for the Land Girls who had been ill. Now that is another story for another day and another time.

THE END